# THE COMMODORE

# THE COMMODORE (Levy)

## by ROBERT D. ABRAHAMS

### Illustrated by ALBERT GOLD

*Philadelphia*

THE JEWISH PUBLICATION SOCIETY OF AMERICA

1954 — 5714

THE
JACOB R. SCHIFF
★ LIBRARY ★
OF JEWISH
CONTRIBUTIONS TO
AMERICAN DEMOCRACY

*Library of Congress Catalog Card No. 54-7437*

*Copyright 1954 by The Jewish Publication Society of America*

*All Rights Reserved*

*Manufactured in the United States of America*

*Sail forth—steer for the deep waters only,*
*Reckless, O soul, exploring, I with thee, and thou with me,*
*For we are bound where mariner has not yet dared to go,*
*And we will risk the ship, ourselves and all.*

*O my brave soul!*
*Oh farther, farther sail!*
*O daring joy, but safe! Are they not all seas of God?*

—WALT WHITMAN

## 1

HE WAS a tall, swaggering old man, and he pushed his way through the crowd that milled about the corridors of the White House as though he owned it. Dressed in the well-tailored uniform of an officer in the U. S. Navy, with gold epaulettes denoting high rank, there was nevertheless something Oriental in his appearance. It may have been the swarthiness of his complexion, or the bristling mustache which he fingered now and again as he walked with that quarterdeck stride of his. It may have been the look of the hawk in his eyes that gave him that touch of the East, but it was not a look of the langorous Orient which he had, rather that of a corsair chieftain.

The single guard at the door eyed him sharply as he passed, but the naval officer did not pause.

"Commodore Levy," he proclaimed to the sentry, "Commodore Uriah Phillips Levy, come to see the President."

# The Commodore

The guard made no attempt to halt him, but continued to stare as the Commodore entered the President's residence to join the throng already gathered in the rooms within.

In that April of 1861 the White House was always crowded. The inauguration of President Lincoln had unloosed a flood of office seekers, and the almost immediate outbreak of the Civil War had brought thousands of strangers to Washington, each intent on telling the new President what to do about the rebellion. There were patriots and crack-pots, idealists, and self-seekers in the crowd. Clamoring politicians sought appointments from cabinet positions to postmasterships of small western settlements. Businessmen with interests in the South wanted to know what the Government was going to do to protect their investments. Old soldiers and sailors, some of them dressed in antique uniforms, saved since the Mexican War, called to offer advice on the management of the new conflict. Inventors offered to demonstrate great ideas for secret weapons which would annihilate the Secession forces; clergymen arrived to offer spiritual help; and most numerous of all, plain curiosity seekers came to gaze upon, and if possible, talk to the big-boned, homely man from the West, who appeared to be so like themselves and yet seemed so at home in his exalted office.

As Commodore Levy entered, hundreds of such visitors were milling about in the reception chambers: Indians in blankets; frontiersmen in coarse, homespun clothes; dandies in the latest fashions from the big cities in the East.

# The Commodore

To all this, the man in the Naval uniform paid no attention. Less determined members of the crowd fell back before him and soon he was able to make his way through a door to the waiting room where John Hay, the new President's young secretary, selected those who were to see Mr. Lincoln.

There were about a dozen people seated in this inner room and as the newcomer entered, Mr. Hay had just come into the chamber from the opposite end, through the door leading to the President's office.

The Naval officer, recognizing the slim, rather dapper and youthful appearing secretary, strode over to him, and addressed him in a ringing voice. "Mr. Hay, I presume. I am Commodore Uriah Phillips Levy, highest ranking officer in the United States Navy, come to see the President."

Levy? Yes, John Hay had heard of him. Wasn't there some story about a court-martial? He remembered now—there had been a court of inquiry and the Commodore had been cleared. Two or three years ago, wasn't it? Surely the old man couldn't want active service? Why, if Hay remembered correctly, Levy had fought against the British in the War of 1812! The memory flashed through the secretary's encyclopedic mind, and then he said, "I'm delighted to meet you, Commodore. What can I do for you?"

"Want to see Lincoln—something to say to him."

"I'm sure the President will be happy to see you, Commodore. He is presiding over a Cabinet meeting and I'm afraid it may last for some time. Maybe you'd like to come back another time—tomorrow morning?"

9

# The Commodore

"Impossible. No doubt you know I am of the Jewish faith. Tomorrow being Saturday, I have religious duties. I'll wait, until very nearly sundown, if necessary. Came all the way to Washington from New York to see Mr. Lincoln. Blasted commotion in Baltimore when I went through. You'd think the rebels held the town, parading the streets as though they owned it."

Others, waiting in the room, overhearing the conversation, rose from their seats and crowded about John Hay. Was it true that the President was in a Cabinet session? Did that mean they couldn't see him? They had been there for hours.

"Sorry, gentlemen. It is true. It will be a long session, I'm afraid. Since the surrender of Fort Sumter and the call for volunteers for our army, you can imagine that the Cabinet is in session almost daily."

"Well, I'm not awaitin' for the end of that," said one Yankee businessman from Connecticut.

"Cabinet meetin' indeed. What in tarnation is the good of a meetin'? Meetin's won't stop the rebs. Why, I hear tell they're comin' up on the Virginny side o' the river in a day or so—mebbe today and ridin' across the Long Bridge across the Potomac and then they'll take Washington and the President hisself and the hull Cabinet. Meetin' is it? What we need is soldiers and guns, not meetin's." The Yankee stamped from the room.

"He's right," said another man. "Who is guarding this White House itself? A parcel of amateur soldiers—no more than a posse of militia, self-appointed and littering up the floor of the building. Why, they're sleeping on the carpets outside this room. I had to pick my way over

# The Commodore

them to get in here. I'm leaving, too, I'm not getting trapped in the White House by any reb cavalry." He left as the Connecticut man had done.

Others decided to depart less violently, and in a moment Commodore Levy found himself alone in the room, except for John Hay.

"You'll excuse me if I go to work," said Mr. Hay pleasantly, seating himself at his desk in a corner of the chamber.

"Certainly, do not let me disturb you," replied Commodore Levy, "I am an old hand at waiting." He settled himself in the most comfortable chair in the room and sat very straight and self-possessed.

Hay worked steadily at some papers. The only sound was that of the scratching of his pen on the documents. For a few minutes, there was no interruption.

Then, a veritable tornado of noise broke the quiet as two boys ran into the room. They were the redoubtable Lincoln boys, Tad, 12 and Willie, 10.

"Why, boys, what's the matter?" John Hay demanded.

"We want Pa," Willie exclaimed. "Tad just broke a looking glass with a ball. I told him Pa wouldn't care."

"But I said he would," exclaimed Tad, "because it isn't Pa's glass. It belongs to the United States Gov'ment. But it's seven years bad luck if you don't throw salt over your shoulder, so I did and it just about ruined the carpet and now I got to see Pa and have him say the Lord's Prayer backwards so as to take away the bad luck."

"Now calm down, boys," Hay admonished them. "Your Pa is in a Cabinet meeting."

# The Commodore

"Well, then, can you say the Lord's Prayer backwards, Mr. Hay?"

"No, I can't," John Hay replied, laughing.

Tad noticed the Commodore for the first time. He ran over to him. "Say, that's a beautiful uniform. Almost as fine as a Zouave's. It's Navy, isn't it?"

"Yes," the Commodore replied.

"This is Commodore Levy," John Hay introduced. "Tad and Willie Lincoln, Commodore."

The Navy officer solemnly shook hands with the President's young sons.

"Say," Willie demanded, "can *you* say the Lord's Prayer backwards to help us out of the bad luck?"

"I can't even say it forward," exclaimed the Commodore, smiling.

The two boys looked the uniform up and down.

"Commodore. That's higher than Captain," said Tad. "Same as a General in the Army, isn't it?"

"It is," Levy replied.

"Golly, I want a lot to go to sea," said Willie, "but Pa says I'm not old enough. I'm nearly eleven."

Nearly eleven. Uriah Levy's mind went back in time . . . he had been nearly eleven that day in Philadelphia . . . so many years ago . . . in 1803 . . .

# 2

IT WAS Sunday morning in Philadelphia in the summer of 1803. Eleven year old Uriah Levy walked along Dock Street looking with avid interest at the many ships which lined the quays.

He was seeking the brig *Van der Meer* out of Curaçao, in the Dutch West Indies. His small hand clutched a letter from his grandfather, Jonas Phillips, which Uriah was to give in care of the master of the Dutch vessel for delivery to the President of the synagogue in Willemstad. Grandfather Phillips was President of Congregation Mikveh Israel in Philadelphia, and there was steady correspondence between the two Jewish communities, whose roots both went back to the Sephardic congregation of the Netherlands.

Uriah cared nothing about the letter. What was important was the opportunity to visit the docks and gaze at the beautiful vessels which came from so many far-off ports, and see the sailors, and feel a part of the romantic

13

# The Commodore

world of the sea toward which the mighty Delaware carried the ships.

The port on Sunday morning was almost deserted. Most people in the town were in Church. Even many of the seamen on the ships were ashore to worship, leaving only a watch to prevent possible boarding by thieves and pilferers.

Uriah whistled as he walked. He knew by sight almost all the ships which frequented the River, from the coasters which sailed up and down the shoreline of the young Republic, to the big merchantmen which voyaged around the Horn to the far Pacific.

The *Van der Meer?* He knew she generally berthed at the dock at the foot of Chestnut Street. Yes, there she was, and from the look of activity on her deck, just preparing to sail. The Dutch sailors were storing cargo in her hold and her mate was standing on the deck, shouting orders in Dutch to the perspiring mariners.

Uriah walked to where the gangplank from the vessel touched the shore, and called out.

"Is Captain Maartens aboard?"

"Ja, ve sail vid de tide."

"Please give him this letter."

"Ja."

How Uriah wished he was sailing with them. Some day he would. Grandfather Phillips, who was a merchant and dealt with many a shipowner, had promised him.

Grandfather loved the sea, too. It was he who had first taught Uriah how to tell one rigging from another, and the differences in the lines of the various vessels. They had had many fine walks together along Dock Street,

# The Commodore

Uriah and his grandfather, ever since Uriah was old enough to walk at all. Grandfather was old-fashioned in some ways; he still wore knee breeches and a three-cornered hat instead of the newer fashion of long trousers and a stovepipe, but the boy loved him dearly. Grandfather told wonderful stories—not only about ships but about the War of the Revolution and how he had been a friend of General Washington himself. How he had invited the General to his daughter Zipporah's wedding and how the General had danced with Uriah's Aunt Zipporah after the ceremony. Grandfather Phillips knew other tales, too, such as the one about his own grandfather, Dr. Nunez, who had been on the *Charming Nancy,* one of the first ships to come over, bringing the founders of the city of Savannah, in Georgia. Yes, Grandfather was a great man, who sat upon the pulpit at the Synagogue on Cherry Street on Sabbath mornings, as President, or as they said, Parnas of the Congregation, but who also liked to make friends with the sailors along the docks on weekdays.

Uriah knew his grandfather had allowed him to be the messenger to carry the letter to the Dutch captain just so he would have an excuse to see the ships. Uriah's mother and father weren't too happy about their son's enthusiasm for the sea. There were better interests for a Jewish lad than ships, his mother said. What better interest could there be, Uriah wondered?

Look at that tall, three-master over there. Wasn't she a beauty? Uriah hadn't seen her before and he walked her length, admiring her lines and puzzled by her unfamiliar rigging. How he would love to command such a vessel—or sail aboard her in any capacity. How big she looked alongside the little coaster at the next dock!

A sailor, seated on a barrel on the coaster's side of the wharf, called to Uriah.

"What do you be doing there, boy?"

The boy regarded the man. He was a big, bronzed fellow, wearing a bandanna on his head, gold earrings, blue trousers and a red jersey.

"Just looking at the ship, sir," Uriah replied. "She's a beauty."

"Danish, out of Copenhagen," said the sailor. "Aye, she's right enough. But how is it you ain't in church this morning like all good Philadelphians? Never saw such a churchy city—between your Quakers and the rest."

"I'm Jewish. I don't go to church."

"Jewish, is it? Well, well. Me, I'm a free-thinker, not holding much with any religion. My Bible is Tom Paine, I always say. What's your name? Mine is Sims, Billy Sims, able seaman, at your service."

"Uriah Phillips Levy, sir. I hope to be a sailing man someday."

"You do, do you? That I never yet met, a Jewish sailor."

"I know a lot about ships," Uriah explained. "I know how to box the compass and tie sailor knots, and the names of all the sails, and port from starboard. I like all that better than the day school or the Hebrew School. I can't wait to go to sea."

"Well, what are you waiting for? Tied to your mamma, mayhap?"

# The Commodore

"My father says I'm too young. He thinks I may change my mind. After my Bar-Mitzvah—that's when I'm thirteen—he says we can discuss the matter."

"Sailing folk don't ask no man's permission," said the sailor. "You can't really be wanting to go to sea, or you'd up and go. Now, if you was to come to Billy Sims and say 'Billy Sims, able seaman, wouldn't there maybe be a berth aboard a certain coaster as a cabin boy'—why Billy Sims would scratch his head and say—'happen there might be a place a board this very coaster, the *New Jerusalem,* out of Savannah.' Ha, Ha, Cap'n Wilkins would be appealed to by you, that I'm sure. A holy fellow, Cap'n Wilkins, well versed in his Bible. That's why he named his ship the *New Jerusalem.* Well, if you'd like, come on board and say to Cap'n Wilkins, 'Sir, I'm a Jew and a Jew belongeth in Jerusalem,' and by the beard of Neptune, he'll very likely sign you on. 'Specially since we happen to be lacking a cabin boy, the latest having run off when we reached this port."

Uriah's eyes were shining. To sail away on a coaster! Perhaps visit Savannah, the southern town Grandfather Phillips had so glowingly described to him—a town where Palmetto trees grew, and where the darkies sang sweetly in the nighttime. But would his mother and father allow?

"Please, sir, Mr. Sims, could a boy sign on for just one voyage?"

"That would depend on how Cap'n Wilkins looked at it. If the Cap'n said 'yes,' yes it would be. If no, then negative, as the saying goes. Go on aboard and ask him.

# The Commodore

You'll find him areadin' of his Bible in the master's cabin."

Uriah found himself unable to resist the invitation to walk the gangplank and set foot on the ship.

The *New Jerusalem* was a small coaster, carrying two masts, but she was very clean and scrubbed-up looking. Uriah looked with curiosity about the neat deck, the well-coiled ropes, the spick-and-span paint. He found the captain's cabin and timidly knocked at the door.

A cheery voice called to come in, and Uriah entered the small cabin, to behold a white whiskered old man seated at a green baize covered table, a large Bible open before him. He looked up over his glasses and saw the boy.

"Well, lad, what is it that brings you here of a Sunday morning?"

"Please, sir, I'd like to sign on for a voyage, if you'll have me."

Uriah was astounded at his own daring. What would his parents say? He was the second oldest of seven children, with another coming, but that didn't mean his parents wouldn't want him to stay at home.

"Well, well, sign on for a voyage, eh," Captain Wilkins' eyes twinkled. "What is your rating? Mate? Bo'sun?"

"Oh, no, sir, I'm only eleven. But I love ships and some day I'm going to be a sailing man. I heard you might be wanting a cabin boy."

"So I do, so I do. Tell me, what is your name, and where are your parents? I'll not be accused of forcing you into the service like a British man-o'-war."

# The Commodore

"My name is Uriah Phillips Levy, sir. My parents have others at home."

"Uriah, eh? That's a good name out of a good book. Tell me, which Uriah are you?—Husband of Bath-sheba? High Priest to King Ahaz? Prophet of Judah? Son of Koz? or the one who stood at the right hand of Ezra?"

"Why, none of those, sir, just Uriah Phillips Levy of Front and Cherry Streets, Philadelphia."

"And the Phillips. Are you related to the Jew broker Phillips?"

"My grandfather is Mr. Phillips, a broker, sir."

"Well, well, I know him. He deals very fairly. He is very learned in the Bible as well. So you'd like to go to sea, would you?"

"Yes, sir."

"Do you know the work's hard and the pay never much?"

"Yes, sir."

"Do you know the might of a storm at sea, and how a good sailor cannot be sick, even if he would be?"

"Yes, sir."

"Will not your grandfather be angry if I snatch away his scion for my cabin boy?"

"He will say so, sir, but he will not be. He knows I wish to go to sea."

"Well then, young Uriah, I have a mind to sign you on. Mind though, no running off, if I do. And you must write a letter to your parents, telling them where you have gone so that they know."

"But if they know, they'll stop me, sir."

"Billy Sims will give the letter to a tavern-keeper

friend of his to deliver to your mother after we have started sailing down the Delaware. We sail tonight for Savannah with the tide. Think you can be ready?"

"Oh, yes, sir."

"Best not leave the ship then, or you may change your mind. Get along aft to the galley, Uriah, and tell the cook you're the new cabin boy of the *New Jerusalem*.

## 3

THE only act of his life which Uriah Levy ever regretted was in sailing away as cabin boy without telling his parents about it first. "I should have been tormented by the devil himself for that," he said afterward, "putting my dear mother in such a worry, and making my father suffer. Oh, they got the letter, but there was no excuse for having left like that. The only plea I can make in justification is, I was only eleven and the chance seemed a glorious one and not to be missed. Besides, I wrote again, from Baltimore, the very first port we put into on the way to Savannah, and sent it off by the fast stage, and told them both I loved them very much, and Grandfather Phillips, too; but I always regretted that I had not told them I was going before I went, especially since it was nearly two years before I came home again and I never saw my grandfather, since he died while I was away. But, outside of the first

# The Commodore

unhappiness I caused my parents, I've never regretted anything else in my life."

The *New Jerusalem* was a fine little coaster. She was sturdy as her captain, and her crew consisted mainly of honest and decent men, a cut above the scum who often manned the ships in those sailing-ship-days. Captain Wilkins was a just man and an excellent ship-master, who needed no cat-o'-nine-tails to enforce discipline as he sailed from port to port up and down the coast from Massachusetts to Georgia.

Uriah did not enjoy washing pots and scrubbing in the galley, but after the homesickness and seasickness wore off, he loved the rest of his life on the sea. His chores were hardly more than what he had been called upon to do at home. He told the cook, who was a New York man, "My mother was one of twenty-one children of my Grandfather Phillips. Every child had his chores in his house. She expected the same from us."

"It's lucky you are to have a mother," the cook exclaimed. "Me, I'm a orphan. Never went to school. Nobody to look after me, except Cap'n Wilkins. Went to sea with Cap'n Wilkins ten years ago—he taught me much from the Bible, changed me from a miserable sinner to a saved man as doesn't touch rum, gamble, or use profane words."

"Cap'n Wilkins often talks to me about the Bible," said Uriah. "Thinks I ought to know more about it, being a Hebrew. I told him I'm not supposed to know all about it until I'm *Bar Mitzvah*. That's when I'm thirteen and I become a man."

"Ha, ha, a man at thirteen, are you?"

# The Commodore

"Yes, I am, and Cap'n Wilkins is telling me I must go home for the *Bar Mitzvah* and study so that I can be made a man in my religion."

"And how is it you can be a sailor, lad? I always heard the Jews can't eat with Christian folk. Sets their stomachs on edge or something. Yet you seem to enjoy your food, right enough."

"I don't eat pork or shellfish," said Uriah proudly. "I can't help it if I must eat what is considered not clean in our religion in order to go to sea. Someday, when I am a ship-master, I will have other food, maybe—"

"Ship-master, is it. How long will it be until then, lad. Maybe a year or two?"

"Don't tease me, cook. I will be a ship-master some-day. Maybe a sailing-master in the Navy. Oh, that would be the life, on board a full-rigged man-o'-war. None of your coasters then."

"Man-o'-war is it? I'd rather be dead than serve on a man-o'-war," exclaimed the cook. "Did you ever see a sailor get twelve lashes on a man-o'-war, just for failing to speak politely to an officer or some such?"

"Lashes?"

"Aye, with a cat. It's not a pretty sight lad. They say we're a free country, but no man is free aboard a man-o'-war. Stay away from the Navy, lad. If you must go to sea, go in a merchantman."

"No, cook, when I'm grown-up I'll go with the guns, and the flag, and the big white sails. But I'll not be hit with any cat. I would rather drown than be beaten."

"Then stay off a man-o'-war. But stop the chatter now and peel the potatoes, Mr. Uriah whatever-your-Jewish-

23

name-is. I mean no offense to you, lad. It's just that I can't remember any name out of the common."

"That's all right, cook. Cap'n Wilkins sometimes calls me Uriah, the Hittite. I like that because Uriah, the Hittite, was a brave soldier."

So it went, as the *New Jerusalem* sailed up and down the coast.

Young Uriah visited all the cities. He saw Baltimore, Charleston and Savannah in the south, New York and Boston in the north. He saw how great was the new nation to which he proudly belonged. He saw, too, from time to time, the few ships of war of the tiny United States Navy, and how the sailors of the Navy when ashore misbehaved far worse than the merchant seamen. They were the scum of the cities, and many of them showed the marks of the lash on their backs.

Yet Uriah loved to see a proud frigate of the line sailing along, her colors flying, her sails set, her gun ports showing the muzzles of the long guns. He thought how fine it would be to command such a ship! To sail to foreign ports, to sweep the seas instead of sailing only in coastal waters. He would be known as the Jewish Captain, and be admired when he went to Synagogue in the ports he visited.

So Uriah spent nearly two years of his boyhood on the *New Jerusalem,* learning a sailor's ways, unconsciously learning justice and mercy from the kindly, if stern, Cap'n Wilkins and his mates and crew.

One day while they were lying in the Port of Boston Uriah was busy cleaning up the captain's cabin when Wilkins entered.

# The Commodore

"Uriah," he exclaimed, "I've just had my owner's orders; we're bound for Philadelphia this trip and in good time. Remember how you signed on for but a single voyage?"

"I do, sir, but—"

"But you've stayed. You're a good boy, Uriah and I believe some day you'll be a good sailing man. But it's time you went home and followed the way of your faith. There is a Jew broker in Boston, very like your grandfather was, Uriah, a good man. I happened to see him today and spoke to him of you. He says it takes a good six months to prepare a boy for his confirmation in your religion and if you are twelve and a half, as I described you, it would be a wicked thing for you to delay. He knew your grandfather; he had heard of his death as you had—every congregation up and down the coast knew of it. He wanted me to bring you to him and leave you ashore here. He says for the sake of your grandfather's memory he would receive you into his own house for the preparation, but I say there's more to it than that, lad. You must go home, like the prodigal son in the Good Book, and may you bring joy to your father's house. Yes, Uriah, in Philadelphia we shall find a new cabin boy. When you have finished your stay at home, if you wish to come back to the *New Jersusalem*—it may be I can find you a berth as ordinary seaman. Would you like that?"

"Indeed, sir, I would."

"Then be a good boy; I shall leave you in Philadelphia, and in a year or so, you may come back to us. You will be very learned in your Testament by then, and ordinary seaman Levy may teach something of the Bible to his ship-master."

Uriah was pleased and excited. To be an ordinary seaman was to be a part of the real sailing crew. There would be no more work in the galley then; he would climb the rigging, set the sails, and do all the tasks of a sailor. He hoped he could endure the time ashore. He wanted his Bar Mitzvah, too. It would be wonderful to stand up before the whole congregation and feel like a king in Israel. How the other boys would envy him. They had never been to sea. What dull lives *they* had lived. Yes, it would be very pleasant to be back in Philadelphia for a little while.

He was doubtful what his reception at home would be. Although he had written brief letters a half dozen times when he had been in port, he had never been able to give a return address to which his mother or father could have written. He had learned of his grandfather's death only by accident, through talk with a young Jew in Savannah who had proved to be a distant cousin of Uriah's.

Jonas Phillips' death had grieved the boy very much. When he heard the news, he had a sudden flood of memories of the old man; his kindnesses, his adventurous spirit, his tales of olden days. He wondered if, without the influence of his grandfather to moderate his parents' displeasure with him, they would receive him at all.

But as the *New Jerusalem* rounded Cape May and came up the Delaware, Uriah felt for the first time the happy joy of the home-coming adventurer. Later, when he saw the church spires and red-brick buildings of his native city coming into view, he could not repress his delight.

After the *New Jerusalem* had docked at the Chestnut Street wharf and all had been made ship-shape aboard, he rolled his few belongings into a bundle, shook hands with Cap'n Wilkins, the mate, and bo'sun and the crew, and, assuming his most sailorlike swagger, walked down the gangplank and along Dock Street. How much he had seen and done since that Sunday when he had delivered his grandfather's letter to the *Van de Meer*. He felt very much a man.

But as he turned up Cherry Street and walked the last block to Front Street, he found himself walking faster and faster. How good the brick front house with the so-carefully-scrubbed marble steps looked to him.

Then he was at the door, and a moment later, in answer to his knock, there was his own mother.

"Uriah," she murmured, and then she grasped him tighly to her. The sailor was home from his first long voyage.

★
★ ★
★ 4 ★
★ ★
★

THERE were a new brother and sister to meet; there were six brothers and sisters with whom to renew the ties of affection—and to impress with salty lingo and maritime tales of ships and ports; there was a forgiving father and a loving mother; there was the preparation for the Bar Mitzvah.

The preparation had been thorough. Uriah's father had found a teacher to instruct the young sailor-on-shore.

The teacher, Amos Hart, was recently arrived in Philadelphia from London. Born in Holland, he spoke with a strange accent of London-over-Dutch, which at first amused Uriah, but the boy soon grew fond of the swart, jovial newcomer and forgot his accent in his interest in what the teacher had to say.

Mr. Hart was employed by a ship-furnisher, and knew much about the sea. He taught Uriah after hours and enjoyed explaining religion to the eager, adventurous

youth, so much wiser in the ways of the world than his
stay-at-home contemporaries.

When it came time for Uriah to learn the ancient bene-
diction over the Torah—

> "Blessed art Thou oh Lord our God, King of the
> Universe, who hast given us a Torah of truth
> and implanted within us Eternal Life. Blessed
> art Thou oh Lord, the giver of the Torah,"

it had special meaning for him.

"Eternal Life, Uriah," Amos Hart would explain, "life
which has its tides like the sea, yet goes on forever, this is
the life promised of old. And the Torah to which you
will dedicate yourself, is it not the ship of life to us, upon
which we sail forever upon the seas of God? All human
hope is in that ship, Uriah—and it shall bear us safely
through every storm."

At last, after many lessons, the great day came when
Uriah, having reached the age of thirteen, stood before
the congregation. That day Uriah was proud and his
parents were proud. He stood before all a man in his religion, and for the remainder of his life, he was never to
forget how he felt at that moment—that feeling of being
a sailor upon a greater ship than any he had yet known,
and of setting sail upon a limitless sea.

Then, the Bar Mitzvah was over, the congratulations
given and accepted. The great day passed and it was time
to think of more worldly affairs.

Cap'n Wilkins had, of course, long since departed from
Philadelphia aboard the *New Jerusalem*. Uriah did
not know when he might return, but he made no secret

of his determination to return to his seafaring life as soon
as the vessel came to Philadelphia.

Michael Levy, Uriah's father, lacked the understand-
ing of the boy's ambition which Grandfather Phillips
had had, and he had been deeply grieved by Uriah's conduct in running away, but now that he realized how determined his son was to follow the sea, he became more
sympathetic in his attitude.

One day, shortly after the Bar Mitzvah, he said to
Uriah, "I have been looking into a career for you, my
son."

"Thanks, Father," Uriah replied, "but I know what I
wish to be. I wish to be a ship-master."

Uriah could not express in words what he really
wanted; adventure, the sight and sounds of strange ports
and far-off places; the look of strange people; and most
of all the wish to belong; to be a part of the life of his
country, and to carry its banner to the world.

"But to be a common sailor is nothing," his father
pointed out. "You cannot be one of those rum-sodden,
casual mariners. That is not the way our family lives,
Uriah. We are not rich, but we live decent, honorable
lives. The sea, it seems, is a profession, like any other. I
own it seems a strange one for my son to follow. I should
have preferred you to be a merchant, a lawyer, or a physi-
cian—but since you are determined to go to sea, I am resolved that you shall receive a proper training."

"Cap'n Wilkins will train me well, never fear."

"No doubt. But I have been investigating. I can do
better for you, Uriah. There is a most respectable merchant of my acquaintance, Mr. John Coulter, who is a

shipmaster. He is willing to accept you as an apprentice, as soon as you have turned fourteen. He will send you to sea on a fine merchantman, the *Rittenhouse,* commanded by Captain James Moffit, than whom no man stands higher in the profession."

The *Rittenhouse!* Uriah had seen her. Built Baltimore Clipper style, she could show her heels to any ship of Philadelphia registry. And an apprenticeship to a shipowner. Why that meant in four years he could be an officer in his own right. How Uriah Levy strutted with pride at the idea.

But Cap'n Wilkins. Wouldn't it be disloyal to the man who had given him his chance?

A few weeks later, by happy accident, the *New Jerusalem* came back to Philadelphia. Uriah immediately went on board. Once again it was a Sunday, and Uriah smiled as he found the ship-master seated before the open Bible as he had first seen him, and as he had seen him on so many Sundays since.

Quickly he told the Captain of his opportunity. The old man seemed touched.

"I've had many a cabin boy in my day, Uriah, but none who ever came back to tell me his plans. I like you, Uriah. You're loyal, and that's more than most. You're a lucky lad, if you sail under Moffit. Aye, you'll see Europe and the West Indies, in his ship. You go with my blessing, Uriah. And now that you're a man in your religion, stand up for it as I do for mine. It won't always be easy." He rose and shook the boy's hand. Uriah wanted to cry, but he knew he was a man and must not. So he

# The Commodore

gulped, "I'll be thinking of you and the *New Jerusalem,*
sir, I promise."

He came down to the dock again to watch his old vessel sail. But further along at the Southwark dock was the
proud *Rittenhouse.* Yes, he could wait until he was ready
for his apprenticeship to sail on her.

At last his fourteenth birthday came, and proper articles having been signed in a lawyer's office, Uriah was
taken by Mr. John Coulter and placed in the care of Captain Moffit. For the next four years his services belonged
to Mr. Coulter. He could send him where he would.

The *Rittenhouse* was thrice the tonnage of the *New
Jerusalem* and was sailed with much greater formality.
Uriah found the life hard, but he was contented. He had
set out on the voyage he had sought, and in the *Rittenhouse* he travelled for nearly two years along the long
sea lanes. He saw Dublin, Edinburgh and London, and
ventured down to Spain. He voyaged to the island of
Hispaniola, to Antigua and St. Lucia and the other
islands of the West Indies. Because he carried his Jewishness with him as a sort of challenge, he was sometimes
unpopular with some of his shipmates. Sailors are endless debaters, and sometimes in the fo'csle, when the men
were off watch, the everlasting talk of women and good
times ashore would pause, and the debate would turn to
religion. When that happened, Uriah would sometimes
interrupt his elders, insisting on presenting what he believed was the Jewish point of view on this or that question of theology or doctrine. Often, the men would
thereupon make him the butt of their wit.

# The Commodore

One sailor in particular, a lad only a little older than Uriah, was especially offensive.

Ned Ott was a big, blonde, coarse-looking ordinary seaman and resented Uriah's apprenticeship which would finally lead to his becoming a merchant officer rather than a seaman.

One day when the off-watch talk turned to the Bible, the question of Jonah and the whale was discussed. Some thought "whale" must be a mistranslation. No whale could swallow a man. Others contended, whatever it said in the Bible, must be true. Another, who was a freethinker, said the story was silly and proved that the whole Bible was nonsense.

Uriah broke in to say, "The Hebrew word is not 'whale,' it is 'fish.' "

Ned Ott exclaimed, "And Jonah was thrown off the ship because he was a Jew-boy like you, Levy."

"And the Lord saved him," said Uriah.

"You think the Lord is good to Jews, don't you? Tell me, is he good to all them thieving peddlers what steal from good honest Christians?"

Uriah flew at Ned Ott and began pummeling him. The others made a ring and watched as the two boys struggled over the fo'csle deck. At length Uriah prevailed and sat astride the panting Ott.

"Take it back?"

"Won't. Dirty Jew."

Uriah pummeled him some more.

The noise of the affray became so loud that the bo'sun suddenly appeared.

# The Commodore

"Here, no fighting, you," he shouted, and pulled Uriah off his opponent.

Taking each boy by the ear he hauled them both out on deck.

"What's all the row," he asked?

Uriah explained, "He called me dirty names."

"Did not," said Ned Ott. "Called him a Jew—he is one, isn't he? Brings bad luck to a ship like Jonah did."

"Looky, Ott—I don't care if he's a Iroquois Indian, full of warpaint. He's a sailor on an American ship and he's got as much right there as you have. Maybe more, seeing as how he's apprenticed to the owner." Then he made the boys shake hands.

Uriah was learning every day, often by his mistakes. After his fight with Ott, he wasn't quite as free with his talk when the conversation turned religious, but he carried a chip on his shoulder, nevertheless. And the further he voyaged, the more he loved the life and wished for the day when he would have a command.

Then, in 1808, after two years of Uriah's apprenticeship, the United States, angered at the way in which the British Navy stopped and searched American ships and even took members of their crews and forced them into the British Service, declared an embargo on all shipping from United States ports. This meant that no foreign ship was allowed to enter an American harbor and no American ship could sail to a foreign port.

The *Rittenhouse* had to return to Philadelphia without cargo, and her crew was discharged, to become part of the discontented band of shipless sailors who now hung about the docks at which so many fine vessels were lying useless.

Uriah raged with the rest. How dare the British behave as though the states were still colonies? Why, Mr. Coulter would be a poor man if his ships couldn't sail.

But Mr. Coulter was quite philosophic about the situation. After Uriah had come home to his parents and made the acquaintance of still another newborn baby brother, he reported to his master.

John Coulter conducted his business on the ground floor of his house on Second Street. Uriah expected that since he could not continue to sail in the *Rittenhouse* he would have to work as a clerk at Mr. Coulter's. But that man of affairs had other plans for him.

"Uriah, I have heard good reports of you," he explained. "Captain Moffit says you are a far cut above the rest, although he says you are of a proud and sometimes quarrelsome nature."

"I cannot abide being baited for my religion, sir. And if any man slurs the United States, I feel as angered as if he slurs my religion."

"Good for you, lad. Too many of our youngsters have forgotten what their fathers fought for and endured so that you could have a country. I fear it may not be long until we may have to fight a second war for independence, and if we do, it is on your generation we must depend."

Uriah's eyes were very shiny. "If that should come, sir, you must release me from my indenture so that I may join the Navy."

The shipowner smiled, "Still bent for the Navy, are

you? That won't please your father. It is my hope and prayer that the British will come to their senses without war. Uriah, I have in mind, while you are bound here in port by the embargo, to send you to school—to Talbot Hamilton. He is an old British naval officer, but a loyal American. How would you like to study navigation? Mr. Hamilton conducts the best school in the country, I have heard."

"Oh, sir, I would like that very much."

So Uriah went back to school and for nine months worked diligently at navigation, drawing and nautical theory. From Talbot Hamilton he learned more than navigation. Hamilton was more than a sailor. He had many interests; he was a collector of paintings, especially those of naval engagements. He liked Uriah and allowed him to visit his picture gallery, pointing out not only the naval features of the pictures, but also the artistic. Uriah was much interested. He enjoyed drawing, himself, and was fascinated when he found that art, like navigation, had its techniques. And Hamilton was fond of saying, "The best officers are not the roughest. A real officer is also a gentleman."

Then a reluctant United States Government came to the conclusion that the embargo was doing more harm than good, for the lack of foreign goods was causing great hardship to the farmers who made up most of the American population.

When news of the end of the embargo came, Uriah believed he would return to the *Rittenhouse,* but John Coulter decided otherwise.

Now that he had learned navigation, even though he

# The Commodore

was still an apprentice, Mr. Coulter told him he was sending him out on another and much smaller ship, the brig *Polly and Betsey*. She did not sail to Europe, but was mainly in the West Indies trade, and the 'but' sent Uriah into an ecstasy of happiness. Uriah was to sail not as a seaman aboard her, but as her second mate! He was an officer at the age of 17. He was on his way.

The day he walked aboard the *Polly and Betsey* was like another Bar Mitzvah. Then, he had become a man in his religion. Now, he was a man in his profession.

## 5

WHEN he had less than a year to go before finishing his apprenticeship, Uriah made a voyage to the West Indies in the *Polly and Betsey*
which ended in disaster for the young second mate.

Having put in at the Island of Tortola in the British
Virgin Islands, Uriah was sent ashore by Captain Silsby,
the master of his ship, to purchase supplies.

Tortola was a flourishing port; the harbor of Road-
town was famous for its brawling sailors—ashore, for its
rum, and its sugar plantations which were owned by rich
planters who spent much time carousing in the town.

Uriah loved the islands; to go ashore and see the tall
palm trees, smell the pungent spices with which the
winds were laden, see the fancy equipages of the planters,
and the smiling faces of the Negroes, made the young
mate feel a part of the great world of romance.

On this particular trip ashore, Uriah had completed
his business, and while awaiting the sending of a small

# The Commodore

boat from his ship to fetch him aboard, he relaxed at a table in front of a waterfront tavern drinking a cup of local coffee. The trade wind was blowing a gentle coolness across the sun-warmed isle. It was February. At home now the Delaware was probably frozen over, and the houses damp and cold. How good it felt to sit here and watch the world of the Indies saunter past.

There was a British sloop-of-war, the *Vermyra,* in the harbor, and Uriah could not help but admire the seamanship of her crew as he watched her long boat ferrying back and forth to the quay. Like all American seafarers in those days, he had no regard for the British, whose acts had caused the embargo which had kept American ships idle in their home ports for so many months.

At a table next to him two British officers were sitting. They were from one of the many English vessels in port. The two men were somewhat tipsy. One of them noticed the *Polly and Betsey* in the harbor, and seeing the Stars and Stripes standing out from the staff at her stern, exclaimed, "Shouldn't let a Yankee ship in a British port." The other officer said, in agreement, "Shouldn't let her fly their rebel rag here, either."

This was too much for Uriah. He leaped to his feet and strode over to the British officers.

"It happens that the 'rag' you refer to is my flag. I'll not have my country insulted."

The two officers looked the youth up and down.

"Who asked you?" the first officer inquired in an insolent London drawl.

"And who might you be?" the second asked in the same offensive manner.

# The Commodore

"Uriah Phillips Levy of Philadelphia, second mate of that same *Polly and Betsey,* and apprentice to Mr. John Coulter."

"Levy, Levy," said the first officer. "No wonder Yankee ships sail so badly—if your sort is an officer."

The second officer pointed to his own nose, laughed and cried out "Ole clothes? Any ole clothes today? Gif de besht price for ole clothes!"

The first officer roared with laughter at his companion's gibe at Uriah's Jewishness.

"The Yankees have fallen pretty low," he exclaimed, "if they're using Jew peddlers for mates. How much will you take for your flag, mister mate?—Two shillings and sixpence?"

Uriah forgot the teaching of Talbot Hamilton that an officer must be a gentleman and tore into the two men. Flailing about him with both arms, he pushed both the British off their chairs and each sat down heavily on the ground. With each hand he pushed the face of one of his tormentors down to the earth.

"That's a present from the Jew peddler," he shouted at the first. "And that's a gift from an American mate," he screamed at the second.

Then he turned and strode away.

Tortola was a British possession, and it seemed to Uriah that he had better board the *Polly and Betsey* at once.

He looked toward his ship, but the long boat had not yet put off from the vessel, and it would be some time before he could make his departure from the shore.

# The Commodore

He glanced over his shoulder and saw that the two British officers had risen to their feet and were brushing off their uniforms. At the same time, they were calling loudly for assistance.

Uriah had no wish to be arrested and perhaps miss his ship.

He knew it would probably be an hour or more before the long boat, as prearranged, came for him.

He saw a waterfront tavern, not like the one at which he had encountered the British officers, but a grog shop of a lower order. He went inside, thinking to find concealment there.

The usual riff-raff of a West Indian port were carousing at the bar. All manner of sailors, both merchant and from the British naval vessels were gathered there.

Although Uriah seldom touched rum, he ordered a drink so as not to appear conspicuous. He sat near a glass-less window hole in the wall, giving a view of the *Polly and Betsey* so that he might observe the putting off of the long boat and make a dash for the dock as soon as she had tied up. He wondered if the British officers would inform the authorities of his assault and send a search party for him. He decided they probably would not, for it would be humiliating for them to describe the incident.

A half hour went by, and Uriah remained in the close, humid tavern, while the assembled sailors drank, gambled at dice, sang, and brawled among themselves. Suddenly a little Negro boy came running into the tavern and said something in a low voice to one of the sailors.

Instantly a number of men rose and ran through the

# The Commodore

back of the bar, evidently meaning to escape through the rear of the building. Others sat where they were and laughed heartily at the sudden departures.

Uriah did not understand what was happening and made no move to leave.

A moment later he learned the reason for the commotion when a British Sergeant, followed by a file of marines, entered the tavern.

They are looking for me! Uriah thought. The officers have reported the incident. I will be arrested and tried by a British court! What should he do? He glanced out of the window. There was the long boat, putting off from the *Polly and Betsey* at last, but it would be twenty minutes at least before she reached the shore.

The Sergeant called out—"Nobody is to leave this place. Any foreigners here, or are you all British?"

Uriah did not say anything. Perhaps he would be overlooked by the men, who were now scattering about the room, looking over the occupants.

He felt in his pocket for his seaman's document and the duplicate of his apprenticeship papers which he carried for identification. If they searched him, they'd know him right enough.

He sat perfectly still, but the Sergeant finally arrived before the table at the window where Uriah was and said, "Your name and papers."

Uriah did not know what to do. He decided to break for the dock and hope the crew of the long boat would see him. He would plunge into the water, if need be, and hope to be picked up.

# The Commodore

He leaped from the table at the Sergeant's words and jumped through the window.

Immediately, the whole squad rushed after him through the door.

Uriah ran as fast as he could, but it was not fast enough. A fleet marine chased him and tripped him up, and then felled him with a blow on the head with the butt of his musket. He lost consciousness.

## 6

WHEN Uriah regained consciousness, he was in the foul-smelling hold of a ship, and from its motion, he knew that the vessel must be under way. For a moment he could not remember how he had come there, but then he felt the large lump on his head and recalled his attempted flight.

He was dizzy as he looked around him. A half-dozen other men, in various states of consciousness, were lying on the floor near him. Two or three appeared to be in a drunken stupor. One was moaning with pain and had a blood-stained bandage wrapped around his leg. Another was sitting quietly, his back to the wall; as Uriah's eyes grew accustomed to the gloom, he could see that this man was staring at him.

"Where am I?" Uriah asked.

"British sloop-of-war *Vermyra*," the man answered. "Press gang caught you. Caught me, too. Now, we're for it—so are the others here. We are, so to speak, all in the same boat. I'm Samuel Handy, late of the merchantman *Channel Queen,* out of Bristol."

"Press gang, eh," murmured Uriah. "I thought the marines had come for me especially."

"No, not looking for you particularly. Just looking for sailors to put in the navy. I wish I was dead. I served once before in one of His Majesty's ships. A good sober man, I am, but I won't be sober long now."

"But you're an Englishman," said Uriah, "whereas I'm American. How dare they press me on to a British war vessel?"

"I don't know how they dare, Yankee, but as you can see, they do dare."

"Why—I'll see the captain. I've heard of such impressments, but there will be plenty of trouble for His Majesty if I'm not released."

"Maybe you'll have President Jefferson put on another embargo, eh, just a'cause of you," Samuel Handy exclaimed.

"Thomas Jefferson is a great man," Uriah replied, "and His Majesty already knows he has a long arm. However, he won't be President after this month. We have a new man taking office—James Madison."

"Twill be all the same to us common sailors," said Handy—"your Jefferson, your Madison, our King George (God save him!). What do they know of how it goes with the likes of us."

"I'm no common sailor," insisted Uriah. "I'm second mate of the brig *Polly and Betsey.*

47

# The Commodore

"Second mate, is it? I did see that ship in harbor. She has good lines. But it will be all the same, Mister Yankee, mate or no, you'll be a seaman on this ship."

It wasn't long after that that the bo'sun of the British ship came to the hold and blew his little pipe. Walking through the huddled group of drafted men, he pushed and kicked into consciousness those who were in a stupor.

"All of you, rouse and up on deck to take the oath and join up."

Uriah found himself being propelled, against his will, to the deck of the ship, where an officer was standing by the foremast.

All the men shuffled up to the officer who, without even looking at them, said, "You are all sworn in. Raise your hands."

Uriah kept his hand by his side.

"Sir," he said, "I cannot take your oath. First, I do not swear with my head uncovered, nor on your testament, for I am a Hebrew. Second, I do not swear allegiance to your King, for I am an American."

The officer looked at him in amazement.

"A Yankee Jew is it you are? Well, you're here now and we're far at sea and you'll work your way or starve."

"Work, I will, but swear I'll not. I demand to see your commanding officer. I am mate of the brig *Polly and Betsey* and you will answer to the government of the United States."

"That I will, when they catch me," the officer answered. "But come now, I'm an Irishman myself, and not one of your Britons, but I have my orders. I wish the press gang would find out that every man ashore isn't His

48

# The Commodore

Majesty's subject, but somehow they don't. There's some would throw you overboard, if you refuse to swear, or let you sweat in the hold, but I'll not. I like your spunk, Yankee Jew, that I do. Go to work, with the rest, but the log shall show you didn't swear in, and first chance I get I'll have a word with Captain Scobel, dashed if I won't."

Then Uriah was dragged away with the rest and turned over to the anything-but-tender hands of the bo'sun.

For two days he labored as a common seaman, biding his time, hoping for an opportunity either to escape at the next landfall or present his case to the Captain. Then to his surprise, a midshipman came to the fo'csle where Uriah was off watch, and shouted, "The Captain orders Levy to report to him."

Uriah found Captain Scobel alone in his cabin. He was an inspiring figure of an officer.

Uriah stood before him, very straight and calm, as the Captain addressed him.

"I have heard an extraordinary tale, young man, that you are Yankee, a Jew, and a second mate."

"It is true, sir."

"Have you any proof?"

"I have, sir."

Uriah fished in his trouser pocket and brought out his "safe conduct" issued at Philadelphia and the duplicate of his indenture.

Captain Scobel looked them over with interest.

Then he said, "Strange. I've never seen a Jewish sailor before. Don't misunderstand me, lad. There's no reason why you shouldn't be one. Why, at home in Plymouth and Southampton most of the ships' furnishers are Jews.

# The Commodore

And do you see that spyglass of mine!" He pointed to the long glass hanging on the wall of his cabin—"That's the best spyglass I've ever seen, and it was especially made for me by a Jewish friend of mine, a Mr. Ezekiel Ezekiel of Exeter. Very clever man—besides scientific glass, he paints very good portraits, as well. He wouldn't by chance be any kin of yours?"

"Unfortunately, no, sir, as far as I know, though I have relatives throughout the world, I have been told. My grandfather was at times a ship furnisher, though his principal busines was that of broker, in Philadelphia, where I come from."

"Mr. Ezekiel wouldn't take pay for that spyglass," the Captain mused. "He gave it me on my return from the Battle of Trafalgar. I was a Lieutenant in Lord Nelson's fleet on that great day. Mr. Ezekiel is a very patriotic man. He gave it to me because I came from Exeter, and he said it was fitting to honor any Exeter man who was out with Nelson. Now I shall repay Mr. Ezekiel in some small way by trying to do something for you, lad. But there's no way anybody else but Admiral Cochrane himself could release you. I'd be accountable to the Lords of Admiralty in London if I started to release 'pressed' seamen just because they refused to swear. Why, there'd be more claiming to be Jews and Yankees than admitting to be honest Englishmen. But you're in luck, lad, we're bound for Jamaica and a rendezvous with the Admiral's Flagship. I'll see to it that your case is presented to the Admiral, myself. Are you willing to work your way to Jamaica?"

# The Commodore

"Gladly, sir, if I don't have to swear, or take allegiance to your King."

"Good. I promise you Admiral Cochrane shall hear your story."

After two miserable weeks in the *Vermyra*, she came at last to Jamaica and the rendezvous.

True to his word, Captain Scobel arranged for Uriah to see no less a personage than Admiral Sir Alexander Cochrane himself.

That great sea dog was sympathetic.

"I don't know why we can't sail our ships with our own," he exclaimed. "We impress a dozen of you Yankees, and very likely we'll have a new war on our hands. It's enough that we have to fight the 'frogs' without taking on the Yankees as well. Not that I mind, but His Majesty's government might. Very well, Levy, you shall be put ashore and can make your way back to your ship or the United States as you please. Mind the pirates don't get you on the way. You're only safe from them on a British ship, you know."

Uriah was overjoyed. When he returned to the *Vermyra* he asked permission to present himself to Captain Scobel.

When he thanked the English officer for his intervention, the Captain said, "I don't see why you don't switch your allegiance to us, Levy. I can see a good future for you, even a commission in His Majesty's Navy. Your kind ought not to be working for a farmer Republic which can never amount to anything."

"Thank you, sir. I am much flattered," said Uriah. It

# The Commodore

*was* flattering to be told that he might attain a commission in the premier navy of the world, but—"I have been born to the flag I mean to serve," said Uriah.

"Very well then, lad, go back to your Philadelphia. Mind you, though, we'll be dropping in to burn the the town one of these days, if you Yankees goad us too far. Yes, and your village capital you call after General Washington, too."

## 7

TWO MONTHS later Uriah was back in Philadelphia, telling the story of his misadventure to the sympathetic John Coulter and the ready ears of his parents and brothers and sisters.

Seated in the Congregation Mikveh Israel on Sabbath morning he was conscious of the envious eyes of his boyhood companions, and of the whispers that went around as the story of his impressment, and escape, from the British service was told and elaborated. Yes, God had been good to him, Uriah himself felt and said special blessing for Ezekiel Ezekiel of Exeter, for having made that excellent spyglass and for presenting it to Captain Scobel. He said another thanks to Providence that the two British officers whose faces he had pushed into the dirt at Tortola had not been officers from the *Vermyra*.

It was not long after Uriah's return that the *Polly and Betsey* returned to Philadelphia, and Uriah was sent out again to voyage in her. Soon after, his term of indenture was finished and Uriah was free to pursue his own career.

Now, free of his apprenticeship, but still working for his benefactor, John Coulter, Uriah became First Mate of the *Five Sisters,* and on that ship made profitable voyages. His parents, wishing nothing from him in the way of support, and Uriah being almost constantly at sea, and not caring to spend his money on drink or the usual dissipations of sailors, Uriah found himself, at the age of twenty, with a sufficient sum saved to enable him to purchase an interest in a ship of his own, the 138 ton schooner *George Washington* and to sail as her Master.

Thus, before he had legally reached manhood, Uriah Phillips Levy found himself a full-fledged sea captain, and owner of a third interest in the vessel he commanded.

How fine it was to walk the deck of the schooner and to recollect that the boy who had run away as cabin boy only nine years before was now a prosperous mariner, able to command, and with apparently the chance for a long and brilliant future in the seafaring life.

Because of his youth, it was sometimes difficult for officers and men, often many years his senior, to defer to his leadership.

On the third voyage in which Uriah took his ship to sea, he sailed across the Atlantic. The trip was a profitable one, and when Uriah hove to in the open roadstead of the Isle of May, one of the Cape Verde Islands, off the coast of Africa, he went ashore there to buy supplies preparatory to the long voyage home; his hold was filled with a valuable cargo, including a large sum in gold and a shipment of Canary wine taken aboard at Tenerife.

# The Commodore

Uriah knew that his co-owners would be very pleased with the success of the voyage, and his own share of the venture would come to a sizeable sum.

Yet he had a vague feeling of unease as he went about the business he had on shore, purchasing supplies and obtaining the necessary documents. The mate, Samuel Tully, a much older man than he, had seemed somewhat insubordinate during the latter part of the journey. Tully had been mate under a previous captain and resented Uriah taking command. He carried out orders correctly, but he had a trick of raising his eyebrows while saying, "Aye, aye, sir," which seemed to say, "Very well—but Tully could do better." Once Uriah happened to pass the ship's galley and overheard the mate talking to the ship's cook, "That's what we get for having a Jew cap'n. Do you know every morning and night, cook, when he is alone in his cabin, he twists a cord around his arm and puts some kind of a charm on his forehead, and then says some of them mumbo-jumbo Jew words?"

Uriah burst into the galley and said, "And what is it that you object to, Mr. Mate, in my following the laws of my religion? What is it that you were telling cook we get for having a Jew for captain?"

Samuel Tully had turned scarlet, and then said, "Begging your pardon, sir, I was just saying to cook as how your praying has brought us luck on the voyage."

"From now on you will discuss both our luck and my religion with your captain and not the ship's cook!" exclaimed Uriah and stormed from the galley.

Uriah resolved to replace Tully as soon as they had returned to Philadelphia.

# The Commodore

He had left his ship in the roadstead, it being impossible to dock at the shore. "It's just like at Tortola," he thought, "although I'm in no danger of impressment now." Still, he felt he would be happier when he was back on board his ship. He had come ashore in a small boat, rowed by three of the crew, one of whom remained with the small boat while the other two accompanied Uriah to carry his purchases back when he should have finished.

He was standing in front of the ship chandler's establishment on a street at right angles to the harbor, when he was surprised to see the sailor he had left in charge of the small boat coming toward him on the run.

"What's the trouble, Thomas?" he called.

"Please, sir, captain, the schooner does seem to be making sail."

"Making sail? Without me? Impossible, I gave no order."

"Come and see, sir, she looks like she's ready to up anchor, with her sails set."

Uriah and the sailors ran down the street and looked out across the water. The sailor was right. The *George Washington* was undoubtedly preparing to sail away without Uriah!

"Piracy," he cried. "There goes her anchor now. It's Tully. He'll hang for this, and so will any other who helps him."

The three sailors and their commander stood helpless. What could they do? They could not hope to catch the ship in their small boat, and if they could, they would arrive to be at the mercy of those on board. If Uriah were to give the alarm to the authorities, they might send out an armed vessel to intercept the *Washington,* but wouldn't there be salvage money to pay? And how soon could a pursuer put to sea? Yet, she must be pursued.

"Come with me," he commanded. "We will report to the harbor master."

Worse luck, most of Uriah's own money was on board the ship, and he had spent nearly all he had with him ashore.

On the way to the harbor master's house he questioned the three sailors. Had they heard anything of a plot? "I warn you to speak up, if you have," he thundered; "for piracy is a hanging matter, the worst crime a seafarer can commit."

Two of the sailors insisted with evident sincerity that they had heard no whisper of any plot. The third said, "Cap'n, to be sure I thought it was naught but a joke, but cook did say as how it was whispered that Mr. Tully and two others had been talking about how valibel the cargo is we're carrying, and how easy it would be to up anchor and sail away with the gold and the drink to the West Indies, where there's plenty of islands to hide in and no questions asked."

"The West Indies, is it? And why did you not think to tell this to your captain?"

"Why, sir, I thought it was only talk, Mister Tully being somewhat of a big talker, sir, begging your pardon. I swear I never thought he'd do it. Would I be here now, sir, if I were in on it?"

# The Commodore

"No, you wouldn't," Uriah admitted. Tully and two others. They would hang for it, that he swore, but would that save his ship?

The harbor master was found and was sympathetic. There was no naval vessel nearby which could be sent in pursuit of the *Washington*.

The disconsolate Uriah, after taking statements from the three seamen to be used in court if he ever found the piratical mate and brought him to justice, paid off the men with most of his few remaining dollars, and managed to secure passage aboard a schooner to the West Indies, with a draft drawn on his banker in Philadelphia.

"Shouldn't you go back to Philadelphia first and confer with your partners?" the owner of the schooner asked.

"Not without either my ship or Samuel Tully," said Uriah grimly.

## 8

THE proverbial needle in a haystack is an easy find compared to one small schooner, hidden away among the thousands of islands and reefs which dot the Caribbean Sea.

Yet Uriah, from his previous intimate acquaintance with the region, was able to deduce the probable course and possible destination of the pirates.

She might head for Tortuga, that island off the coast of Hispaniola, long beloved of buccaneers. She might make for Saba, the odd, hat-shaped island, whose valley in the center concealed a sizeable town which could not be seen from the sea. She might make for one of the Virgins, or for the Pearl Islands off the North coast of South America. But there was the ever present doubt that she had headed for the West Indies at all, for what proof had Uriah that the islands were her destination, other than the gossip repeated by a single frightened sailor?

Yet, Uriah's luck, so bad when he lost his ship to the

piratical Tully, was to help him now, for in Jamaica, the island to which he had secured pasage, he immediately had news of the *George Washington.*

The captain of an American ship in the harbor of Kingston, Jamaica told him that only a few days before, at the Island of St. Lucia, he had seen three men who had come ashore in a small boat, claiming to be the only survivors of the schooner *George Washington* which had struck a submerged wreck off St. Lucia. They explained the master of the vessel went down with the ship. They had brought casks of wine and bags of Spanish silver dollars ashore. They had been questioned by the British authorities who had found nothing suspicious in their story.

"They'll feel differently when the master of the *Washington* turns up alive," Uriah exclaimed.

Uriah secured passage on an inter-island sloop and sailed to St. Lucia.

St. Lucia was a green and beautiful tropical island. Because of the extensive fortification in its circular, land locked harbor, it was sometimes called the Gibraltar of the West Indies.

But Uriah's thoughts were neither on the beauties nor military strength of the harbor, as he landed at the dock in the town of Castries.

Castries was a small place, and the first person Uriah addressed, a Negro roustabout on the dock, confirmed that Tully, and two others from the *Washington* were living in the town.

"Very sad story, sah," said the Islander. "He master o' he

ship drownded in de wreck. He sailors, too. Only lef' de cook, wan sailor, and de mate."

Uriah agreed that it was a sad story, even sadder when he recalled that there had been four, not three, men on the ship when she sailed away without him!

He walked up the wide and only important street of the town and suddenly came upon none other than the cook!

The cook turned pale when he saw Uriah. He stood rooted to the spot, unable to turn and flee.

Uriah walked up to him and exclaimed sternly, "Villain, I have found you. Where is Tully?"

"Why—why—" the cook stammered. "I never saw you before. Who are you?"

"Play no games with me, sir, or you'll hang as well as Tully. Tell the truth and it may go better with you than the others."

"Oh, Mister Levy, have mercy on a poor cook, brought away from his duty by a piratical officer," the man whined, his attitude changing to a cringing one.

Uriah took him by the shoulders and looked the frightened man straight in the eyes.

"Speak up, man, the truth. Where is the *Washington?*

"Scuttled, sir, if it's the truth you want. Twenty days out of the Isle of May—one day out of St. Lucia. Mister Tully it was who ran away with your ship. He forced me to go along—me and Dalton and Yates. They went willingly enough, but I didn't, that I swear, sir. Look, sir, you'll help me, won't you, if I tell? You'll see I don't hang? And protect me from Mister Tully?"

"I think you will not hang, if you tell all, and I promise

you I'll protect you from Samuel Tully," said Uriah grimly.

He led the shaking man to a tavern and demanded a full confession.

"Tully said we'd be rich, sir, when we up anchored and sailed away. It was a very hard voyage—I had to stand watch like a mariner, and cook as well, we being only four. Twenty days out, Mister Tully ordered us hove to, and says: 'according to the chart, we should be but a few leagues off St. Lucia in the Windwards. We'll scuttle ship here, taking the wine and money ashore in the small boat, say we struck a wreck, and that the Master and the other three mariners drowned.' Oh, it was a wicked thing to do, sir, but what could a poor ship's cook do to stop the mate? You'll see I don't hang, sir, as you promised?"

Uriah nodded his head and the cook continued.

"So Mister Tully put the casks and the money in the small boat, and he took a auger and bore holes in the ship's bottom, and the water commenced to rise in her, and then Mister Tully and Dalton and me, we rowed away and came ashore. On the way the mate divided the money—him and Dalton got big bags of it, and me, they give a small bag, me being a small man, you see, with no real part in the doings."

"And Yates?" asked Uriah.

"Oh, sir, that's the worst of it. Yates is dead."

"He wasn't dead long when you scuttled. Three men couldn't have sailed the *Washington*.

"No, sir, he wasn't dead long."

"When? When you left the ship?"

"No, sir—the night before. But I took no part in that, sir, upon my honor, I didn't. Tully and Dalton done it. Tully used the knife and Dalton helped to throw poor Yates overboard, so that there'd be one less to divide with, now that the voyage was done. I been in deadly fear Tully would kill me, sir, since we come ashore, not for the little share they gave me, but for fear I'd tell. Why I was down to the Port this morning, sir, trying to sign on as cook on a ship so that I could get off this cursed island and leave them two behind. But you'll see I don't hang?"

"So it was not only piracy, but murder," exclaimed Uriah.

"But not by me, sir, not by me. What do you mean to do now, sir? Be careful, if Mister Tully sees you, he may kill you, sir, and me too."

"I might kill him," exclaimed Uriah. "Running away with my ship. Stranding me and the rest of the crew. Murdering Yates. Scuttling my ship. Ruining me and my partners. Yes, I might kill him, if it weren't that I'd rather see him hanged. Come, cook, we're going to the Captain of the Port and you're going to tell him what you told me."

The trembling cook, still invoking Uriah's promise that he wouldn't be hanged, went with him to the British Captain of the Port. The Englishman was not too friendly at first to the American, but when he heard that piracy was involved, his attitude changed. Civilized men of different nationality might hate each other, but they were all united in hating pirates.

The Captain of the Port secured the help of a squad of English marines and went in search of Tully and Dal-

# The Commodore

ton. Both were found drunk and asleep and were taken without a fight.

They were sent to the United States in irons, in the first ship going North and were landed at Martha's Vineyard, Massachusetts, where they were tried.

Uriah attended the trial. True to his promise, he persuaded the authorities to allow the cook to turn state's evidence and go free. Tully and Dalton were convicted and sentenced to hang. President James Madison commuted Dalton's sentence to life imprisonment because it was apparent from the evidence that Tully had dominated him and that Tully alone had planned the crime.

Samuel Tully was hanged.

**9**

TULLY was hanged but that didn't raise the *George Washington* from the bottom of the sea. At twenty years of age, Uriah was a master without a ship, but he did not care, for during the time when Uriah was in Massachusetts attending the piracy trial, the long smouldering quarrel with England had broken into open warfare and Uriah had determined to serve his country in the struggle which would ensue.

He applied for a warrant as sailing master in the Navy. This was a petty officer rank, usually held by a mariner of long experience. It was, however, inferior to that of midshipman, the grade from which officers were usually commissioned. Uriah chose it in preference to the midshipman rank because it gave more promise of immediate action at sea.

On October 21, 1812, Uriah was appointed sailing master by President Madison's warrant and ordered to active service. For the first time he donned the uniform of the country he loved.

# The Commodore

How proud he was, as he swaggered about Philadelphia. How he hoped for a speedy assignment to a ship. He wished that his father, who had recently died, had lived to see him in his uniform. He showed it off to his mother, who smiled at his vanity and feared for his safety, but rejoiced in his enthusiasm.

Uriah dreamed of being a hero. He would revenge the honor of the United States for the impudent way in which the British had forced American mariners into their service.

He was disappointed (though his mother was secretly pleased) when he was ordered to duty on the sloop-of-war *Alert* stationed in New York harbor. He had not given up being commander of a merchant vessel so that he could spend the war in New York harbor. But now that he was in the Navy, he had to follow orders.

For six months he remained in New York. He spent most of his time on shore. The twenty-year-old Uriah was very handsome in his dress uniform of blue coat and tight white trousers, and the ladies of New York, especially those of Shearith Israel, the congregation in which he attended Sabbath services while he was stationed at Manhattan, were fascinated with him. Uriah enjoyed the hospitality of the Jewish families of New York; he learned dancing and often went to the theatre, but he was restless. The man who had chased pirates from the Cape Verde Islands to the West Indies, and brought them back to Massachusetts' justice, was scarcely content to be a picture book hero who did his fighting in ballroom conversation.

In June of 1813 his chance came. He volunteered for duty at sea and was ordered to join the brig-of war *Argus,*

# The Commodore

Captain William Allen commanding, as sailing master. No harbor duty for the *Argus!* She was a trim little vessel of 298 tons, carrying a crew of 125, and mounting eighteen guns. She was to run the dangers of the British command of the high seas and convoy the American Minister to France, William Crawford, to the French port of Lorient.

"What good fortune is mine," Uriah told himself. Captain Allen had been first mate of the famous frigate *United States.* The other officers were equally renowned.

The American Minister came aboard at midnight so that the British spies who were active in New York might not get word of his departure. The *Argus* sailed with the tide.

Because he was a volunteer, Uriah was not the regular sailing master of the ship, and so he was put to various tasks not ordinarily designated for a sailing master. He inspected the guns—the two "long toms" which were set in holes in the bow of the ship, to be used in a chase in which distance, rather than weight of the shot, was the object; and the sixteen short guns, or carronades, which rested at ports in the ship's hull and were ready to fire a deadly broadside at an adversary. He presided at masthead trials of sailors for disciplinary purposes. He helped the mates with navigation, and assisted in teaching a green crew to handle the sails and rigging.

After only a few days at sea, Captain Allen sent for Uriah.

"Levy," he said, "it's true you're no midshipman, but you've been a merchant captain. I've had my eye on you since we sailed, and I know a good salt-water man when I

# The Commodore

see him. We're short one lieutenant. I'm appointing you to that rank temporarily, for the voyage."

"Thank you, sir," exclaimed Levy, his eyes lighting up with pleasure. Lieutenant in the U. S. Navy, at sea in a ship of war on an important mission. Could a man wish for more?

More than half of the crew had at one time or another been impressed into the British Navy, and those who had had that cruel experience of unwilling servitude in the navy of a foreign flag, were eager for battle with the British. The morale of the crew was good, though even so, it was necessary to sentence a few of the men to blows of the lash.

Lieutenant Levy had to be present on the occasion of such punishment, and this was the sole portion of his new duties which he hated.

"Don't like the lash, do you, Lieutenant?" said Captain Allen.

"No sir, these men are Americans and free men. There should be other ways of discipline."

"Can't say I agree, though I don't like it myself," exclaimed the commander. "Like as not we'll see plenty of action this voyage. We'll be glad then we've licked them into shape, you may be sure."

Mr. Crawford, the American Minister, ate in the wardroom with the officers, and he became quite friendly with Uriah. This friendship was to have pleasant results in later years.

The trip across the Atlantic was, for Uriah, disappointingly free of action, except on one occasion when the *Argus* sighted a small British merchantman at sea and gave chase. The *Argus* fired her long bow guns after the enemy ship, and the ship hove-to and surrendered.

Uriah joined in the cheers of the American crew as the British vessel struck her flag, and it was a proud moment for the Acting Lieutenant when he saw the boarding crew go upon the enemy ship, and run up the American flag where the British ensign had been flying before.

Uriah had a moment of dread when Captain Allen selected the men who would leave the *Argus* and sail the merchantman prize back to New York, but the Captain passed him by with a smile and sent a midshipman and a few mariners to serve as the prize crew.

All went well with the ship, the crew, and the voyage, and four weeks after setting out from New York, Mr. Crawford was landed at Lorient.

That night, Captain Allen called the officers and midshipmen to a council in his cabin.

"Gentlemen, we have orders to sweep the English Channel and harass John Bull on his very doorstep. We sail on a dangerous voyage of great opportunity. God grant we shall be worthy of our country and its flag. Let us pray."

Uriah prayed with the others. Jew or Christian, it made no difference. They were praying to the "God of Battles," each in his own way.

## 10

ON JULY 14, while the French were celebrating Bastille Day with firecrackers, free wine, dancing in the streets, and the singing of the Marseillaise, the *Argus* slipped out from Lorient and headed for the English Channel. When the men realized that instead of heading westward toward home the course was set for the north and east, great excitement gripped them. They were sailing right into the teeth of the British lion, and might feel his fangs, but there was glory in it and to spare, and possible prize money as well, and for many to bring disaster to British merchantmen would be a sweet revenge for past hurts.

Two days out from port, they came out of a typical channel fog to find themselves almost upon a small British lugger. Captain Allen ordered a shot fired across her bow, and a moment later, the British ship, seeing no help in sight and being unarmed, struck her colors.

A loud cheer went up on the deck of the *Argus* as Captain Allen detailed Acting Lieutenant Levy and a small group of mariners to board the prize. In a few minutes, the bewildered crew of the merchantman, who had had not the slightest expectation of encountering an American ship so close to their own home port of Plymouth, had been shepherded aboard the *Argus* as prisoners. Swiftly Uriah examined the cargo, jettisoning overboard what was not of great value, and transferring to the *Argus* a small quantity of coin and some textiles.

Then Uriah and his crew set the British ship afire, hoping she might drift into other shipping and cause havoc in the Channel, while the *Argus* and her prisoners continued on her dangerous voyage.

Two hours later a second lugger was overhauled and the same procedure followed. Uriah, like all the officers and crew, was in a constant state of excitement.

Captain Allen said to him, "Levy, you are like the old war horse in the Bible who smelleth the battle from afar off and saith Ha! Ha!"

"This is what I came for, sir," Uriah replied. He did not say that he was afraid—that each time a ship appeared through the fog, he had the feeling that she might be a big British frigate-of-war.

Captain Allen continued, "It's a strange thought for a Captain to express to a youngster, Levy, but do you know much as I wish for battle and count on victory, I am sometimes fearful, just at the moment we glimpse the foe."

Uriah grinned. "Thank you, sir," he said. "Knowing that makes me feel I am no coward for being afraid."

# The Commodore

"It is no crime to be afraid, Levy," he replied. "It is giving in to fear which cannot be allowed. I'm sure every man on board is frightened, but in action, what does it matter, so long as he forgets his fear and does his duty?" Then he forgot his philosophy as he turned to shout an order.

For four long, long weeks the *Argus* cruised almost within sight of England, burning, pillaging, and making the Channel unsafe. Prisoners from the latest ships to be taken told of the alarm in London.

"Sir," said the disconsolate master of an English ship who had just seen his vessel burned before his eyes, "Captain Allen, sir, in London they think you are the devil himself. Upon my word, at Lloyd's Coffee House they are raising the rates of insurance sky-high because of you."

"And no doubt His Majesty's Navy is out in full force looking for me."

"That, sir, you must not ask me to answer. I have no doubt they'll catch you, though, and I hope to live to see it, upon my oath, I do."

When Captain Allen believed he could not remain longer in the Channel without being set upon by a greatly superior force, he suddenly veered around, sailed westward along the coast of Cornwall, capturing and burning ships as he went, and had the audacity to round Lands-End and sail boldly north into the Irish Sea, which divided Ireland from England and was considered a British lake (at times a very stormy one).

It was in this Sea that on August 12, four weeks after setting sail from Lorient, the *Argus* sighted the merchantman *Betty*. She was a larger and more valuable prize than any yet taken, but like the others, she was unable to make any resistance, and struck her colors.

When Uriah was sent aboard, as usual, he found a very valuable cargo, far too valuable to jettison, and too extensive to be taken on board the *Argus*. He therefore returned to his own ship for further orders.

"Her manifest shows cargo worth many thousands of dollars," he reported to Captain Allen. "The vessel herself could bring a large sum in a foreign port."

"Good. Then we must try to send her to a French port under her own canvas. Lieutenant Levy, you will command the *Betty*. Take a prize crew with you and make for France. When you arrive, arrange with the French authorities to sell the ship and cargo."

Uriah did not like to leave the *Argus,* but he was honored that his commander had chosen him to take the prize to port.

With a prize crew of eight, he set off in the *Betty*. It was now his dangerous task to elude the British naval vessels which were undoubtedly nearby searching for the *Argus,* and successfully to navigate the Channel without being discovered by the British.

That night on the Captain's walk of the *Betty,* with the ship plowing through a rough sea in clear weather, with his prisoners below and only the steersman nearby, Uriah felt great loneliness. He thought of the docks in Philadelphia, and of his walks there with his grandfather, Jonas Phillips. How proud he would have been as a boy had he been able to see the man he was to become, making his way through hostile waters, commanding a captured ship.

# The Commodore

Yet the boy had never been lonely as the man was. Command was always lonely. For those who take orders, there were always others to share them—or higher ones to obey. But for the commander of a vessel, there was no one to share. Suppose a British man-o'-war were to loom up alongside?

But Uriah thought, "If Captain Allen trusts me, I must trust myself." And he thought also, how brave the Jews who had lived before must have been. They, too, had sailed in perilous seas; any Jew who survived in the old days of oppression had to know how to find the wind and sail with it, how to tack and navigate, and how to elude the lurking enemy and bring his prize to port. What was that prize? Uriah asked himself, pacing the dark deck beneath the white sails on the starlit night. What was the prize? Was it wealth? No, certainly it was not. Wealth could be had without adventure, fear and danger. Was it glory? No, many a Jew had brought his prize to port and wanted no glory for the doing. What was the prize?

Then Uriah knew the prize was freedom; the freedom to be oneself, one single self in all the universe, not a great self, perhaps, but a self free to meet the universe—and God—and man as it pleased. Aye, that was the prize all the great Jews had sought to bring to port.

So, slipping through the night in the captured ship, Uriah thought the long thoughts of a young man faced with responsibility and danger.

Thus he voyaged on, but as he stood staring out at the night, master of the swift moving, captured vessel, he murmured the well beloved lines of a Psalm which was his favorite—"Blessed be the Lord my Rock, who traineth

my hands for war, and my fingers for battle; my loving
kindness and my fortress, my high tower and my deliverer,
my shield and He in whom I take refuge; who subdueth
any people under me."

There was little sleep for Uriah that night, nor any
the next day, or the next. Twice strange sail was sighted,
but Uriah was able to turn away unobserved. He was
making very slow progress toward France, due to the constant necessity to change course, but slowly, and, as he
thought, surely, he was nearing his goal.

Suddenly, on August 15, three days after the taking of
the *Betty,* came catastrophe.

The lookout in the rigging suddenly sang out that a sail
was sighted. Uriah ordered course changed to drop below
the horizon and hoped he had not been seen, and if he
had, that the other vessel was a merchantman, not a warship. But in the next several hours, no matter how much
he tacked and veered, three more vessels were sighted, and
suddenly, from one of them, a gun spoke and a shot whistled across the *Betty's* bow.

Uriah turned again and, with a good wind and all sail
set was able to draw away from the hostile vessel, which
turned in pursuit. However, in an hour or so, the *Betty's*
lookout suddenly discovered another sail ahead, and
Uriah had to choose between lying-to and being over-
taken by the first vessel or sailing past the second. He
knew the vessel behind him was hostile, so he had to
chance the one before him.

Very speedily the *Betty* bore down on the approaching
second ship. To his horror, Uriah saw that she was a
British brig-of-war, similar in lines to the *Argus.* He tried

# The Commodore

to turn away, but the long guns of the enemy ship began to sound, and he had no alternative but to lie-to or be sunk. He was in despair. He felt as though he had betrayed Captain Allen's trust in him.

A few minutes later, he had to strike his own well-loved colors and wait to be boarded, to have the *Betty* recaptured, and for him and his crew to be made prisoners.

★

★     ★

★  **11**  ★

★     ★

★

IT WAS a sad but dignified Uriah who stepped on
board the British brig-sloop *Pelican,* and was brought
before Captain John Fordyce Maples, her commander. "You'll find some companions of yours below,"
said Captain Maples in a not-unkind voice. "Yesterday
morning we took *Argus.*"

Uriah started. The *Argus* taken!

"Your commander is dead. A brave man, Captain
Allen. The first lieutenant also is dead. The fortunes of
war."

Uriah was led away to the hold. He was visibly shaken
by the news. It was bad enough that the *Betty* had been
lost, but the *Argus!*—And the officers dead!

Being an officer, he was not placed in the hold with the
crew, but in a small cabin, where he found the second
lieutenant of the *Argus,* Lieutenant W. H. Allen (no re-
lation to their late commander).

"Levy," he exclaimed. "So they got you, too."

# The Commodore

"How did the battle result like this?"

"It was terrible, Levy, terrible. The night before yesterday we captured a brig laden with wine from Oporto and
burned her. Unluckily, some of the crew got at her cargo.
You know how tired we all were—no sleep—no rest—constant worry and watchfulness. Add the drink to this and
you don't get the best crew for a fight. At five yesterday
morning we discovered the *Pelican,* which we now know
was sent out specially from Cork to look for us. We could
have escaped, but you know Captain Allen. He would not
run. He shortened sail and ran easily while the *Pelican*
came down on him with the wind. By six we turned and
fired our port guns, and the *Pelican* responded with her
starboard battery, and action began!"

"How was Captain Allen killed?" asked Uriah.

"A round shot carried off his leg, but he stayed on deck
until he fainted from loss of blood. Soon after, Lieutenant
Watson was killed by grape-shot in the head, and that left
me in command. When the *Pelican* bore up to pass astern
of us, I luffed into the wind and got into a beautiful rak-
ing position, if the gunners had only done their duty—
Oh, Levy—it was a disgrace—they were drunk and the
guns were neither aimed nor fired correctly. After that, it
was disaster. Our sails were hit and down, and even the
wheel-ropes were shot away so that we couldn't steer. By
quarter of seven, the *Pelican* was right alongside us. We
were entirely helpless, and when I saw the British preparing to board, I knew that from then on it was murder
and struck my colors."

Uriah said nothing. So the colors had been struck
before the *Argus* was boarded. "*I* would have resisted the

79

boarding and then boarded and taken the *Pelican,*"
thought Uriah. Then he thought—"How do I know what
I would have done if I had had it to do." At all events, it
made no difference now. The *Argus* had been burned and
Captain Allen and many other brave men were gone. He
was a prisoner, and for him the war was finished.

The battle between the *Argus* and the *Pelican* had been
fought in the Irish Sea, off St. David's Head, in Wales, and
the *Betty* had been recaptured by the *Pelican* off Cornwall. Now, the *Pelican* proceeded to dock at Plymouth,
and nearly a hundred American prisoners were brought
ashore.

The people on the streets in Plymouth were not hostile
as Uriah and the rest were marched through the town.
The *Argus* had been feared when she was burning and
plundering English ships, but now that she was no longer
a menace, her mariners were regarded as brave men, and
English speaking ones at that, and no one who watched
them in the streets made any demonstration against them.
Nevertheless, the men of the crew were a disconsolate lot.
They wished they had left the Oporto wine in its casks
the night before the battle; they wished they had given a
better account of themselves against the *Pelican;* in which
case, they might be sailing homeward by now, instead of
journeying toward the dreaded Princetown Prison which
was their destination.

Although he was an officer, Uriah was herded with the
rest in long wagons in which the prisoners had to stand
during the day-long trip to the prison. Uriah, saddened
though he was by his fate, nevertheless looked with curiosity at the Devonshire countryside, so fair in the August

# The Commodore

sun. Already he was wondering whether he would be required to give his parole not to escape, or whether he could succeed in getting out of Princetown Prison and to sea. He remembered that Exeter, where Ezekiel Ezekiel lived, who had made the spyglass for the British sea captain, was nearby to Dartmoor, where the prison was situated. Would Ezekiel help a young American Jew to escape? Uriah put the idea from his mind. No doubt Ezekiel loved this England as much as Uriah loved his own country. Hadn't he given that glass to Captain Scobel in memory of Trafalgar?

As soon as he arrived at the foul and gloomy prison he had to put aside all thoughts of escape, for as an officer, he was offered limited liberty within the prison only on condition that he would give his word not to try to escape. When he saw that he would be locked in a solitary cell if he did not give his parole, he saw no reason for refusing it.

The Princetown Prison had been built a few years before to hold French prisoners of war, and most of the prisoners now there were of that nationality. Situated on wild and desolate Dartmoor, its buildings were dank and unhealthy, its conveniences non-existent. Many prisoners were sick and there were no medical attendants. Daily there were deaths from malnutrition, exposure and disease.

There were several hundred captured Americans. For the most part, they were kept apart from and had little to do with the French prisoners. Among themselves, having given their parole, they were free to wander about within the small space allotted to them, and they spent their time in idle gambling and homesick story-telling.

# The Commodore

Whenever new prisoners arrived, they were besieged by the earlier comers for news of the United States, the war, and the world.

On the night when Uriah arrived in Princetown, he was surprised when a man came walking into the little cell which Uriah was to share with three other officer prisoners.

The man was in rags and looked half-starved, but he spoke in a pleasant voice and shook hands with Uriah as he introduced himself.

"Have I the honor of adressing Lieutenant Levy, late of the *Argus?*"

"You do."

"Good. Now we need but five more."

"Five more?"

"Yes, for a minyan. I am William Wolf, of Savannah, Georgia. You will find here also Morris Russel, Manuel Joseph and Levi Myers Harby—all prisoners in this foul place, and all of our persuasion. Whenever there are newcomers we scan the names with care. You are the fifth—five more and we shall have a congregation. We do not wish anyone ill, but it would be nice if the next ship taken had at least five Jews on board! You must join us at our midday meal tomorrow—regrettably, it will not be Kosher. It will not be much of anything, in fact—but the fault will not be ours for either lack."

The next day, seated with his four fellow religionists, Uriah gave them all the news he could remember of the congregations in the United States—who had married whom, who had died, who had made and lost fortunes, since these earlier prisoners had been enforcedly absent from the world.

To them and to fellow officer prisoners, Uriah also had to give all the latest war news. How Bonaparte was fighting the Allies in Germany and did not seem to be doing too well, and how it looked as though the British, having thrashed "Bony" in Spain, might soon take him on in France itself, a prospect not too agreeable to the Americans. If the British lion succeeded in finishing "Bony," wouldn't she then turn her full fury on the poor, little United States?

Soon Uriah was ill with a kind of malaria endemic in the prison, and when he recovered, had to settle down to doing nothing and awaiting news from recently arrived prisoners with the same eagerness with which they had greeted him. If before he had been brave and rash, now he was to learn patience.

He remained on Dartmoor through the cold, wet English winter, through the next summer and on into the Fall of 1814.

During that time, in spite of all, he managed to keep his sanity and rigorously attempted to discipline his mind. He organized a class in navigation, in which he both taught and was taught by other captured officers. He took lessons in French and French history from a French prisoner in return for English lessons. Yet the time passed very slowly and uncomfortably, and it was with great joy that in the Autumn of 1814 he learned that he was being exchanged and was being sent back to the United States in a shipload of such exchanged men.

# The Commodore

Before he arrived at the port of Norfolk in the States, the peace treaty had been signed. It was a peace without victory, but one which both sides were glad to welcome.

Uriah welcomed it, too, but what was he to do now? Should he return to the life of a merchant seaman he had known before he had entered the service of the United States?

He chose to remain in the Navy.

## 12

I T IS hard to explain to you, Mr. Coulter," Uriah told his old instructor and friend. "It has been hard to explain to my mother. But at Princetown Prison I had sixteen long months in which to think. It is very good of you to offer to back me with a new merchant ship. I appreciate your confidence in me. But I have decided to remain in the Navy."

"I have no doubt that you are fitted for it," said John Coulter. "I have heard that you are to be given a permanent commission as lieutenant, on the recommendation of Commodore Stephen Decatur himself. And you know I was proud of you when you went into the Navy during the war. But the peacetime Navy, that is something else again."

"Why?" asked Uriah, annoyed that his old patron should question his choice. "Is it so base a decision that a man should decide to devote his life to his country's honor and defense?"

# The Commodore

"It isn't base at all," Coulter replied. "It is the contrary; you are a romantic, Uriah. America holds your love and affections as others are held by their ladies! But, if that pride of yours will not resent me too fiercely telling the truth, you will have two obstacles to face in the Navy which others will not have."

"You mean my religion and my failure to have begun as a midshipman."

"Exactly. Nine out of ten of your superiors may not care a fig that you are a Jew, but the tenth may make your life a hell. You know what the meanness of a superior can do to a naval career. And you know also the great prejudice in the Navy against officers who have come up from the ranks."

"Aye, that I know. All the former midshipmen hang together and resent any officer who was not taught the so-called 'tradition.' That is wrong. If we are to have a Navy worth having, it must be a fighting Navy, not a ceremonial one. I will help to break down this midshipman nonsense and hope someday to find that the simple mariner may yet become a flag officer if he has the ability. I have faith that that day will come. As for the religious difficulty, it is most important that I overcome it; not only for my sake, but for the sake of the Navy and the nation—and not only for today but for all time. Believe me, Mr. Coulter, I am not so blown up with my own importance that I believe I can do this alone; but if nobody does it, our country—my country—will suffer. I have the greatest respect for the religion of the Christians and on shipboard I am careful to follow every regulation for the religious activity of my Christian shipmates; but what kind

# The Commodore

of a country would this be if men who loved America were willing not to serve her because of the prejudices of a few? No, it is because I have by reason of previous service a right to appointment as an officer—a clearer right, I believe, than any other, so far, of my religious belief, that I intend to make a point of it. There will be other Hebrews, in days to come, of whom America will have need. I mean to see that they have their chance to serve, by insisting on serving myself."

"Those are noble sentiments, Uriah," exclaimed Mr. Coulter. "I wonder how much you really mean them and how much you intended the sentiment to mask the plain fact that you like Navy life."

"You are very shrewd, Mr. Coulter, and may know me better than I know myself," Uriah replied, "but I truly believe my motives are what I have said they are. If they are not, I deceive myself as well as you."

The disappointed shipowner, who had seen in the returned Uriah a competent and adventuresome partner in future enterprises, said, "Very well then, my boy. But if you ever decide to go back to the merchant commander's rank . . ."

"You are very kind, my friend, as always," Uriah assured him. "But I have already put in for the commission —and believe it will arrive in due course. Meanwhile, I remain a sailing master—since the end of the war I cannot be an acting lieutenant. So I am second sailing master on the *Franklin* stationed here in Philadelphia—and daily I hope for news of my appointment to commissioned rank."

Uriah's hopes were not fulfilled for a whole year, during which he remained as second sailing master of the

# The Commodore

*Franklin,* but on Dartmoor he had learned patience. Meanwhile, it was pleasant being stationed in his own home port, where the whispers of his adventurous past combined with the glamour of his naval uniform to make him an attractive figure in the eyes of the Philadelphia girls, and especially those of Mikveh Israel, where he was once more a regular attendant. He knew that his mother conspired with the mothers of more than one of the girls to marry him to a suitable bride, but Uriah had no intention of marrying. Why, that would mean settling down—perhaps even leaving the Navy to go back into maritime business—and besides, he was quite content to fall casually in love, and out again, in a fashion which suited his romantic nature.

Uriah enjoyed dancing, and danced at many a ball and cotillion. It was at such a dance, an annual affair called The Patriot's Ball, that an incident occurred which nearly put an end to his naval career. He was in uniform, and was dancing a polka, when he suddenly collided with another man who was dancing. There was an awkward moment. Uriah could not understand how the collision had occurred, but assumed it must have been by his fault or by mutual fault.

He exclaimed, "I beg your pardon." The other dancer, a Lieutenant William Potter, glared at him and said in a voice, audible to many in the room, "I hope you're a better navigator at sea than you are on the ballroom floor."

"I have said 'I beg your pardon,' " said Uriah, restraining his anger, and he turned and joined the dance again.

The next time around, to his extreme irritation, he

# The Commodore

was bumped by a person who immediately danced away.
Uriah turned angrily, and believed that the dancer who
had collided with him was again Potter, but he was not
sure.

Men and girls were tittering and whispering. Uriah
colored but controlled himself. The notoriety of a bout
with Potter might effect his chances for his lieutenancy.
In the Navy, an officer was expected to be a gentleman as
well as a mariner.

Uriah turned to his partner in the dance and said
"That clumsy boor will do that once too often."

"Now, now," said his lady, "save your quarrels for our
enemy in war."

But a few minutes later Potter came by again, and
this time with obvious design, again bumped Uriah. Uniform or no uniform, promotion or no promotion, Uriah
turned and slapped his tormentor's face. Then he drew
away, and when a circle of men formed about Potter and
himself, as if hoping for further hostilities, Uriah, recol-
lecting his position, attempted to walk away.

"Cowardly Jew," exclaimed Potter. "Go home and sell
ole clo'es."

"Sir, that I am a Jew, I neither deny nor regret," said
Uriah. "If I am a coward, the enemy did not discover it
in the late war. As for 'ole clo'es', the clothes I am wearing
I wear with more pride in my country than you seem to
have."

Many of the men present now closed around Potter.
Those who had seen and heard Potter's insult were all on
Levy's side. "You're drunk, leave the floor," one admon-
ished him. "You are no gentleman to talk as you do before

ladies," said a second. "Until you learn manners, you had better not dance," a third remarked.

Two friends of Potter's, seeing that he was in danger of further violence from those who took Uriah's part, grasped the sullen and wrathful man's arms and hurried him from the hall.

Uriah had been victorious; the sympathies of all were with him, but he was much embarrassed. In order not to seem to quit under fire, he resumed dancing, but soon after found an excuse to leave the ball.

Outside, Potter and his friends were waiting. Uriah saw them standing under a lamp in the street. Contemptuously he swaggered past them, confident they would not dare attack him, and believing that if they did, he could give a good account of himself.

He was very disturbed by the incident. For such as this man had he given up the comfortable life of a shipowner to cruise in the perilous voyage of the *Argus,* and spent the weary months in Princetown jail?

Then he brightened up. No, it was not for the Potters —it was for the far more numerous others, the decent kind who had gathered around to sympathize and assist him at the Ball.

Uriah hoped he had heard the last of the incident, and went back to his ship.

He was extremely annoyed next morning when one of Potter's friends appeared, bearing his antagonist's challenge to a duel—a challenge which Uriah did not feel he could refuse without a loss of honor.

"Why should this Potter, whom I don't even remember having met before, interfere with me and my life?" he

# The Commodore

asked. "And why should he be the insulted one? It was I who was insulted, but I am ready to forget the incident; I am sure Potter had been drinking."

"He considers that you insulted him," Potter's second insisted. "You slapped him. Please be so kind as to nominate your second, with whom I will confer. Unless, of course, you decline to give him satisfaction. In that case, you would be no gentleman."

"Very well. I shall fight your little boor. But it will be pistols, I suppose."

"Naturally."

"That is sad. I am a sure shot. I don't wish to kill him, just because he annoyed me at a Ball."

"He can take very good care of himself, sir, name your second."

"Very well."

Uriah did not see what else he could do. He was very young, and to be thought a man of honor was necessary to his self-esteem.

"I shall name my second," he said, "but two thousand and more years of civilized ancestors are looking down upon me with ridicule. There is no knighthood, no chivalry—in short, no damned nonsense in my religion, sir. Nevertheless, I'll name a second and help your little man to success in making a fool of himself."

★
★    ★
★   13   ★
★        ★
★   ★
★

THE DUEL was fought in New Jersey, across the
river from Philadelphia, for the laws of Pennsylvania against dueling were more strictly enforced
than those of New Jersey.

Each party had a second; there was a "judge" appointed by mutual consent of the seconds, and a surgeon
accompanied them. Uriah, his second, Aaron Marks, who
was a civilian friend of his, and the surgeon went across
the river in a rowboat, and met Potter, his second and the
"judge" under a cluster of oak trees which marked the
traditional spot for affairs of honor involving Philadelphians.

It was a cold, damp, spring dawn. Uriah was extremely
depressed. What if this fool should kill him, or even
worse, maim him so as to put an end to his seafaring life?
He had not dared to tell his mother or his sisters and
brothers of the challenge. His poor mother! How would
she bear the sorrow of his death, if he were slain? She

would have been brave enough if he had been killed
fighting for his country, but to die as the result of a ballroom brawl! What sort of death was that for a Jew? He
wanted to go down in history as the first Hebrew to be a
high officer in the American Navy, not as the first to
be killed in a duel!

When he saw his adversary, he was even more alarmed.
Potter gave him a look full of malicious hatred. He was
pale and looked frightened, but seemed not at all repent-
ant.

The two men chose their pistols, and the twenty paces
that were to separate them were stepped off by their
seconds. Now that Uriah realized that there would really
be an encounter at arms, his experience in warfare stood
him in good stead. He was suddenly calm and was able
to shut everything out of his mind except the business at
hand. So Potter wanted an affair of honor. Very well, he
should have one, and Uriah would show him that a Jew
could beat him at his own game.

"Has either gentleman anything to say?" asked the
"judge," after the principals had reached the spot from
which each was to fire.

"Nothing," said Potter in a shaky voice.

"I wish to say a Hebrew prayer," said Uriah in a clear
voice, and repeated the Shemah. Then he said, "I also
wish to state that I shall not fire at my opponent for I have
no wish to kill him. I give him warning that I am a sure
shot and suggest that we go home."

"Coward," said Potter.

"Fool," responded Uriah.

The "judge" said, "Gentlemen, no further words,

please. You will turn your backs to each other; when I count three, you will turn and fire. If neither is hit, you will reload and await my further signal to fire anew. If either man is hit, no further shot will be fired."

The principals turned their backs and the "judge" began to count.

"One—two—three."

At three, both turned, but only Potter aimed and fired. Uriah pointed his pistol into the air and shot. Potter's aim was very bad and the bullet did not graze Uriah.

Uriah was relieved. Surely Potter, having failed to hit and having observed that his opponent refused to aim at him, would feel that his honor had been satisfied.

The "judge" cried, "Neither gentleman is hit. Load again."

To Uriah's dismay, Potter grimly reloaded his pistol, so that Uriah was obliged to do likewise.

Again the "judge" counted. Potter aimed at Uriah and missed, while Uriah once more raised his hand above his head and fired into the air. Yet he was enraged. Did the man think he would stand there and be shot at again and again?

Once more the "judge" proclaimed that neither gentleman was hit. Uriah saw with horror that Potter was loading for a third shot. He did not know what to do. Even so nervous and unsure a marksman as his opponent must eventually find the target—and Potter was trying to aim to kill. Almost mechanically, Uriah fired a third and then a fourth shot in the air, while his opponent missed!

Then, as Potter loaded once more, Uriah shouted, "Fool. This is your last chance. I am going to aim for the lowest hanging leaf in the tree over your head to show you that I can kill you if I want."

This time he aimed with deadly accuracy, and a leaf fluttered to the ground.

Now the seconds stepped in and tried to stop the combat, but Potter was completely unresponsive. He muttered to himself in rage, while loading. Uriah also loaded, but said, "Gentlemen, I beg you to stop this madman. His last bullet grazed my cheek. I do not intend to stand here as a target. Stop him now, or I fear I shall stop his dancing days forever."

The maddened Potter, completely out of control, did not wait for the "judge's" count, but fired at the unready Levy, missed again and immediately began to load.

Levy called out, "Stop him, or I must do so." The seconds ran toward the unheeding Potter, who was fumbling with his pistol, which he was having difficulty in reloading because of his rage.

"Stand back," he called to his seconds, "I mean to have his life." They halted, fearfully, as he pointed his gun at Uriah.

Uriah, realizing his danger, aimed and fired. Potter fell, shot through the heart.

The "judge," the seconds, and the surgeon rushed to Potter.

He was dead.

Uriah stood with smoking pistol in hand.

He threw the weapon to the ground. He felt no triumph in his victory, only chagrin. Poor Potter; to die for a cause was noble; to die for a prejudice was—silly.

THERE was uproar in Philadelphia over the duel. Dueling had never been popular in the Quaker City, and since the famous Burr—Hamilton duel, the so-called affair of honor was unpopular with most Americans. Yet many duels were fought every year, and many participants injured or slain.

Uriah's mother was horrified that her son would have taken part in such an affair and had killed a man.

"But Mother, what could I do. He insulted you when he insulted me. I had no wish to kill him."

"But a Jew to fight a duel, Uriah! We are not such brawlers as all that."

"You are right, but I could not help it. And I swear I would not have killed him if he had not gone mad. I was sure his next shot would hit me."

Neither his mother nor public opinion was satisfied, however. When Uriah went to Synagogue, many avoided talking to him.

# The Commodore

His shipmates were of a different opinion. To them, the sailing master had become a hero, a romantic figure, the sure-shot who had wiped away a stain upon his honor. He found himself a hero to his naval companions.

The good citizenry of the town thought otherwise, and Uriah was indicted by the grand jury. Since the killing had not occurred in Pennsylvania, he could not be indicted for murder or manslaughter there, but he was charged with the crime of "making a challenge to a duel."

By this time, the seconds, including the dead man's friends, the surgeon and the "judge" had all been talking a good deal, and had made the facts plain to their own acquaintances. Public opinion turned. What right had Potter to pick a quarrel with Levy, who had had such valiant service in the war, just because of his religion. Where had Potter been when Levy had been out fighting for his country? Here in Philadelphia, dancing, and drinking, and playing at cards. Who wouldn't fight if his religion were ridiculed? And hadn't Levy deliberately allowed his opponent to shoot at him, while he harmlessly fired his own pistol in the air?

A group of prominent citizens, both Jewish and Gentile, addressed a petition to the District Attorney, asking him to have the indictment dismissed, since inquiry showed that Uriah Phillips Levy had made no challenge, as charged, but had been the person challenged. The District Attorney paid heed to the petition and dismissed the indictment.

Uriah's mother was not so easily placated. "Promise me, never again," she insisted.

"Not unless it is entirely unavoidable," said Uriah.

97

# The Commodore

He was too proud to promise, but to himself, he made the promise. Never again.

Would the scandal spoil his chances to secure the commission in the Navy he was waiting for so anxiously? He hoped not. He felt he must be patient—but it was so long in coming.

Then, in March of 1817, the commission was granted and Uriah was able to add the gold epaulettes of a lieutenant to his uniform. He was ordered to remain on the *Franklin* as an officer. How he gloried in his new rank, even even hastening to the studio of a fashionable portrait painter to have his portrait painted, gold lace and all.

Now he was Lieutenant Levy and no mistake. His portrait looked a little vain, more than a little handsome, and very determined. If Potter had seen the portrait, he might have known better than to challenge such a man to a duel.

★
★ ★
★ **15** ★
★ ★
★

BEING a lieutenant on the same ship on which he had been sailing master was not easy for Uriah. The midshipmen aboard, who had previously expected to outrank him, now found that he was ahead of them in the naval hierarchy. Yet, because they had known him and respected him, both as a mariner and as a person, he had no serious difficulties. When the squadron left for the Mediterranean, the *Franklin* was the flagship of Commodore Charles Stewart. He had a number of supernumerary lieutenants on board, including Uriah, and he was to distribute these men to the various ships of the squadron making the cruise.

The fleet made a rendezvous at Syracuse, in Sicily and there Uriah was given orders to report to the *United States*, a frigate of the squadron. The *United States* had the reputation of being a "gentlemen's" ship, in which all the officers had been midshipmen before receiving their commissions, and Uriah feared that he might be coldly received.

His fears were realized when Commodore Stewart sent for him.

"Lieutenant," he said, "I have received an unusual communication from Captain Crane, of the *United States*. In reply to my order assigning you to him, he has the effrontery to ask me not to send you. He says there is harmony among the officers on his ship which might be disturbed by your coming aboard. Of course, I cannot allow Crane to tell me what officer he will have or won't have, and I mean to give him his orders. What kind of la-di-da Navy are we coming to? But I want to say to you, Levy, that you have done your duty on this ship, and will, I am sure, do it on the *United States*. I thought it only right, therefore, to warn you, you may have your troubles over there."

Uriah was alarmed. He had been so happy on the *Franklin*.

"Thank you, sir," he said. "I knew when I was promoted Lieutenant without serving as midshipman there might be some who wouldn't like it. And there are also a few—a very few, sir, I am happy to say—who seem to feel that a Hebrew cannot be an officer and a gentleman in the Navy. This I expected, and it is my task to try to break down both prejudices, each of which I consider harmful to the Navy and to our country."

"I am with you in that, Lieutenant. Good luck to you on the *United States*."

Uriah's words had been brave, but his spirits were low.

# The Commodore

In the close, confined life of an officer on shipboard, it would be very difficult if he was not accepted as an equal by those of equal rank.

He only knew one officer on the *United States,* a Lieutenant Jones, who had been on the *Argus* when he had been on board that ship. Jones had impressed Uriah as a fair and square sort of man. When Uriah reported on board the *United States,* he was received with curt and formal coldness by Captain Crane.

Uriah sought out Lieutenant Jones and asked him about the situation his coming had created.

"Yes, Levy, of course I remember you. I will be perfectly frank. There are eight officers in the junior mess, and except for me, they all voted to have nothing to do with you. It is best that you should know this, even if painful. But their conception of what you would be like was altogether wrong, so they have determined to, as they put it, give you your chance."

"How do you recommend that I behave?" asked Levy, miserable at the thought that the other officers were against him even though they knew nothing of him personally.

"Do your job. Behave at all times as an officer and a gentleman. Do not seek trouble, but hold to strict account the first man who dares to provoke you."

There was a painful moment that night when Uriah made his first appearance at the mess, but Lieutenant Jones went out of his way to put the newcomer at his ease, and before the meal was over, there was a noticeable thaw in the behavior of the others.

# The Commodore

"They find I don't wear horns," thought Uriah, "and that even though I was never a midshipman, I know how to use my knife and fork properly."

Happily, none of the junior officers, who had so greatly feared his coming, gave him any offense, and before long they accepted Uriah, both as an officer and a friend. So unrestrained did the atmosphere become that, in simple curiosity, he was even asked questions about the rites of his religion.

His relations with Captain Crane, who had not wished him assigned to his command in the first place, continued on a formal basis, and so Uriah, more than any other officer on the ship, felt constantly constrained to be upon his good behavior. That he had chosen a profession in which success was difficult for a man of his background, he had known from the start, and every obstacle seemed to him to be overcome, not only for his own sake, but also for the sake of many to come after. He was determined particularly that Captain Crane should have no opportunity to vent his spite upon him because he had been sent to his ship unwanted.

After some months had passed without incident, a new Senior Lieutenant, C. S. McCauley, came on the frigate, his friend, Lieutenant Jones, having been transferred. McCauley was a martinet; with all the prejudices of one who had been a midshipman against one who had come up from the petty officer ranks. When he came on board, Captain Crane received him kindly and said, with a smile, "No doubt you know, Mr. McCauley, that our frigate is celebrated as the vessel which has a Jew sailing master for a Junior Lieutenant."

# The Commodore

Lieutenant McCauley considered this remark, so unusual especially in coming from a commanding officer, as almost a command, or at least a license for him to provoke a quarrel with a breach of discipline by Uriah, and proceeded to act accordingly.

It was not long after he had joined the ship that McCauley, by certain words of his, provoked the boatswain's mate, Joseph Porter, to show the same sort of contempt for Uriah as he himself showed with Captain Crane. Treatment of this sort was difficult when inflicted by a superior officer, but in a petty officer, it was intolerable.

The boatswain obeyed every order of Uriah's, but in a very surly manner. At length Uriah, having given the boatswain an order, and hearing the fellow muttering a comment on Levy's competence, Uriah lost his temper and slapped the man.

Immediately Lieutenant McCauley appeared, questioned Porter and ordered Uriah to his quarters. A few hours later he was served with notice of a court-martial, with charges preferred by Lieutenant McCauley, and trial to be held before Captain Crane.

Uriah was despondent. Once before, when he was a sailing master, he had been court-martialed, on the trifling charge that he had given the ship's boys an order to clear away the breakfast dishes in the officers' mess, without the order being first given by a Lieutenant. Even so small an offense had nearly served to prevent his being promoted to Lieutenant. This new charge might result in his dismissal from the Navy of which he was so eager to be a part.

The court-martial was farcical. Uriah did not deny the

charge, but pleaded his great provocation. Captain Crane then filed a very singular finding. He did not sentence Uriah to dismissal or loss of rank in the Navy. Instead, he ordered him dismissed only from the frigate, *United States*—thus succeeding in ridding himself of an officer it had irritated him to have to take on board in the first place.

However, when the sentence was sent on to Commodore Stewart for confirmation, the Commodore, having thwarted Captain Crane in his first refusal to accept Lieutenant Levy, promptly reversed the sentence. That would show Crane he couldn't play fast and loose with the Navy!

Yet this did not make Uriah's position any easier on the frigate, *United States*. After the incident he continued to serve aboard her, and was extremely careful to give no further opportunity to Captain Crane or to Lieutenant McCauley to do him harm.

One day, while the vessel was in a Mediterranean port, Uriah, having to go ashore, told a ship's boy to have a small boat prepared to take him. Coming on deck and seeing a boat being made ready, he assumed it was his, and prepared to enter. Another Lieutenant said, "Where are you going? That boat is not for you, but for me."

Uriah replied, "The boy told me it was mine, and I believe it is."

A violent altercation between Uriah and the other Lieutenant ensued, as a result of which, another court-martial was ordered. This time, Uriah was undeniably in the wrong. He had not only lost his temper, he had doubted the word of another officer, and, worst of all, had created a scene between two officers in the presence of members of the crew. This time Commodore Stewart could not and would not forgive him, and a fair trial having been had by Commodore Stewart's orders on a vessel other than Uriah's own, the Commodore could only recommend Uriah's dismissal from the Navy.

The proceedings had to go to the President of the United States for confirmation; and to Uriah's delight, after an interval of some months during which he sat disconsolately ashore, trying to steel himself to the failure of his naval career and a return to the life of a merchant mariner, President James Monroe reversed the sentence and restored the delighted and much chastened Uriah to active service as Lieutenant.

He was now ordered to the brig, *Spark,* then at Gibraltar, and served aboard that vessel without incident. Word of his hot temper had spread through the Navy, and there were many who admired him for it. It gave him no pride to be so admired; he wished to be known as a competent and valiant naval officer, not as the duelist, quarreler, and hothead he was reputed to be.

At the end of his service on the *Spark,* he was overjoyed to be ordered to a command of his own and to a duty which promised glory, adventure and real service to the flag he loved. He was ordered to command the gunboat *Revenge,* to take her to the West Indies to seek out and destroy the pirates who were still ravaging the Spanish Main, and to help in the suppression of the odious and illicit trade in the importation of Negro slaves into the United States.

## 16

F OR a Naval officer there is no happier day than the
day he steps on board his first command, ready to
take a vessel of war to sea, in the service of his
country.

True, the *Revenge* was only a small barque, but she
was Uriah's to command. Here was no Captain Crane
waiting for the opportunity to make life difficult for him.
And to be ordered to pursue pirates—this was revenge
indeed upon the marauders, upon whom Tully and Dalton, who had stolen his ship in Uriah's merchant mariner
days, had patterned themselves.

He would make the *Revenge* a model of what a naval
vessel should be, Uriah resolved. No lashing of sailors on
this ship. He would prove to the Navy that a crew could
be disciplined, without the dread cat-o'-nine-tails or other
barbarous punishment.

The notorious Lafitte, the terror of the Spanish Main,
was reported on the loose again, plundering the Carib-

# The Commodore

bean. Uriah dreamed of catching the scoundrel, and coming home a hero, to hand Lafitte over for the hanging he so justly deserved. He hoped for success in capturing slavers, too. He hated the miserable trade in human beings. One of the qualities he most admired in his idol, Thomas Jefferson, was that, although Virginian himself, he had nevertheless taken the lead in the outlawing of the importation of new slaves from Africa.

Yes, it was glorious to have both a command and a mission, thought Uriah on that November day in 1822, when he stepped on board the *Revenge* at Charleston Navy Yard and prepared to take his ship to sea.

Down the coast he took the little vessel. She handled well. The crew was a smart one and the voyage was pleasant, and in almost record time, after calls at the Island of Inagua and at a Cuban port, the *Revenge* arrived at Kingston in Jamaica, where she put in for supplies, minor repairs, and news of pirates or slavers.

How strange it seemed to Uriah to sail into a British-held port, in command of a war vessel! It wasn't like 1812, he remarked to his junior lieutenant!

He had not long to wait for news of Lafitte. He had been in port only a few hours when a delegation of merchants requested him to receive them. Uriah felt very grand, welcoming the five merchants who had been chosen to represent the rest. The Jamaicans filled his little cabin. Uriah was attired in his dress uniform and looked very handsome as he graciously received the deputation.

"Sir," said the spokesman, "Lafitte, whom we call the modern Blackbeard, has been on the prowl. We have sought for an English ship to follow him and destroy him, but the Admiralty sends us none. Your flag is not ours, but all civilized flags are allies against the Black Flag of the pirate, and we hope you will cruise after Lafitte."

"My orders will permit me to do so," Uriah assured them. "Where is the villain?"

"He is somewhere in the Bay of Honduras. He has taken many ships. We are fearful to send out our cargoes. There are American vessels here, as well as British. Sir, will you give us convoy, so that trade can be resumed, without fear of this damnable murderer?"

"For what port do you seek convoy?"

"To Cape San Antonio, at the western end of Cuba. No pirate dares to venture north of the Straits of Yucatan. If you will convoy our ships to the Cape, you might, if you would turn south toward Honduras, go after Lafitte."

"I will do as you wish. I will need two days to refit. Have all the ships ready to sail and we shall take them to Cape Antonio, as you ask."

The convoy was made up and proceeded as planned. The *Revenge,* acting like a sheep dog protecting the fold against wolves, herded no less than eight merchant vessels slowly northwestward through the Caribbean toward the safety of the Gulf of Mexico.

About halfway from Jamaica to Cape Antonio lies the Island of Grand Cayman, and here the convoy put in for possible news of the marauder.

The people of the little island were in terror. Lafitte himself, in his famous brig, the *Second Substitute,* had landed only four days before, had seized what supplies he had needed, and had sailed off southward toward Honduras. His men had boasted that they were off on a new expedition and that the "Mosquito Coast," as the eastern shore of Central America was known, would soon see them.

On receipt of this news, Uriah himself summoned the Captains of the vesesls he was convoying.

"Lafitte has gone south and we must pursue him," he told them. "You will be safe, for he is the only such villain in the seas. You must run for Cape Antonio while I turn toward Honduras and try to head him off."

The Captains agreed and Uriah ordered the *Revenge* to set sail for the south.

Having failed to sight the quarry, the *Revenge* arrived at the little town of Rattan on the Mosquito Coast, and again sought for news. Lafitte had arrived before them and was still going south, plundering and sinking small coastwise vessels as he went.

Uriah lost no time in sailing once more. He calculated that the pirate should be only twenty-four hours sail ahead of him, and with good fortune, he should be able to overtake him. But he had no local pilot on board and there were many reefs and islets in the vicinity where the pirate might hide.

That night the barometer began to drop sharply and Uriah knew that the *Revenge* was in for bad weather. He ordered the hatches battened down and took all possible precautions for the seas in that area were notoriously treacherous. At dawn a tremendous wind came down from the north, a gale of tornado proportions.

The little *Revenge* was tossed to and fro upon the furious sea. Every man aboard, including Uriah, was seasick. The sun never appeared and the day was almost as

# The Commodore

black as night. Hour after hour passed and only the tolling of the ship's bell differentiated one dark moment from another. There could be no thought of continuing the search for Lafitte. The only objective had to be to save the ship from foundering, or from running upon a reef.

For two nightmarish days and nights the terrible storm continued. During all that time, every man in the crew was on deck or in the rigging. Uriah never closed his eyes. Now and again, he prayed. At times he repeated Hebrew Psalms, sometimes he shouted his prayers in English. At other times, he swore loudly, damning the sea which was robbing him of his quarry, and might well rob him of his ship as well.

Again and again parts of the rigging were carried away in the gale. The masts had to be tied in place with so-called "shrouds" of canvas, else they would have come down and left the ship helpless. The crew were half-crazed with fear and fatigue.

Then, after a full forty-eight hours, when it seemed as if neither man nor ship could survive another moment of such agony, the sun suddenly appeared; the barometer rose sharply, the great black clouds rolled away and the *Revenge* rode quietly on a miraculously calm sea!

Resumption of the search for Lafitte was out of the question. There was nothing to do but limp into the Port of Belize, only a few hours sail sail from the position of the *Revenge*.

Uriah called the exhausted men together and gave them sailing orders to proceed. He blessed the name of God who had brought him and his ship safely through their peril.

# The Commodore

Belize, the port of the British colony of Honduras, welcomed the *Revenge* as Kingston, Jamaica had done. The town had escaped the hurricane through which the *Revenge* had passed, but there was a large number of American vessels lying in the harbor, their masters fearful of venturing out without convoy. Uriah called on the British governor and was well received.

"Your ships have been waiting, but it will take them ten days to load cargo and prepare to sail north," the governor told Uriah. "If only you had not been damaged by storm, I would request you to spend that period in continuing after Lafitte. You have no idea what terror that one rascal causes in these waters."

"I know," said Uriah. "And my dearest ambition is to lay hands upon him. The damage to the *Revenge* is easily remedied, if you can give me help. A day or two and she'll be ship-shape again. I cannot delay the convoy once it is ready, but I will spend the week or more we would be waiting searching for the villain. With luck, we may come upon him."

"Excellent. I understand there is $48,000 belonging to your government which is to be delivered on board your ship and taken with you to Charleston."

"So I am informed by the American agent here," Uriah replied. "My orders will permit this, and the money will be safer in a ship of war than in a commercial vessel. We will load the money and take on water and supplies at once and proceed after the *Second Substitute*, if I have your permission."

"Not only my permission, but my gratitude," replied the governor. "However, there is one request I must make—you do not know this coast, Lieutenant. You must take one of our local pilots on board."

"I prefer to navigate myself," Uriah objected.

"I am sure you do, but we know better than you do the perils you would undergo from the reef. I must insist that in British waters you carry the King's pilot. I will give you one who knows every league of the coast and the Keys. He will show you where you may come upon Lafitte and take you safely past the reefs."

Uriah had no choice, and certainly, with only a week in which to search, it would be advantageous to have a pilot on board who would know the likely hiding places of the pirate. So the King's pilot came on board, and the *Revenge* set sail with the pilot giving the navigational orders.

Southward, down the Keys which lined the coast, they went, searching each anchorage the pilot believed might harbor the pirate.

On the third day of the expedition, they came to the little port of Omoa and they were on the scent again. Lafitte had been here only two days before and was gone again, having plundered and sunk a ship just outside the harbor. Some thought he had run for the Island of Tortola, but others said he had serious sickness on board, his crew was rebellious and half of the men were down with fever. Probably their chief would head for Old Providence Island or some isle even further from the scenes of his recent exploits.

Uriah was disappointed. It would be well enough for the world if the animal limped away to die in solitude,

# The Commodore

but Uriah preferred by far the glory of catching him and bringing him home to justice.

He had only a single more day in which to cruise before turning northward again to take out the convoy.

He headed for Tortola, hoping to surprise the pirate in one of the two excellent harbors in that Caribbean islet. Arriving at nightfall, he waited until dawn and then beat into each harbor in turn but there was no ship there.

Poor Uriah was balked of his prize and had to sail back empty-handed for Belize. He did not know that when Lafitte sailed away from Omoa he would never be heard of again. Whether he died shortly thereafter, or escaped to settle down ashore, was never learned.

Back toward Belize voyaged the *Revenge,* still in charge of the pilot.

For two days and nights the vessel retraced its course, and then on the third night—supposedly the last night before arrival at Belize, terrible disaster struck without warning.

Uriah had noticed that they were sailing rather close to the barrier reef which lines the coast a few leagues from the shore and questioned the pilot, but the pilot told him to have no fears, the responsibility was his, not Uriah's, and that he knew his way in those waters as well as Uriah would know the streets of Philadelphia.

In the night, while Uriah was asleep in his cabin, there was a sudden grinding noise. He awoke and ran to the deck to find to his horror that the pilot had run the *Revenge* full on the reef.

There was no time for grief or for blame. Uriah had to

# The Commodore

do everything at once to save his ship before the waves should pound her to pieces on the rocks. The guns were ordered thrown overboard, the water casks floated and everything else possible done to lighten the ship.

In the darkness, it was impossible to calculate the exact position of the *Revenge*. Uriah had sounding lines thrown out, and felt a moment of relief when the stern line showed deep water.

"That gives us a chance to get off, if the hull is not stove in," he cried.

The trembling pilot, whose mishandling of the ship had caused her to pile up on the reef, was at Uriah's side.

"Damn you for a blunderer," Uriah exclaimed. "I wish I had time to thrash you or throw you overboard."

"Let me take a small boat off the stern and see if we can't drag the ship off," the pilot begged.

"Go ahead."

The small boat was made ready and the pilot took her off, a willing crew rowing with all their might, but a few minutes later the boat had to be pulled back to the *Revenge* by the lead rope.

The gasping pilot led the frightened crew to the deck. "The sea is running so high that the boat could not live, not alone get the *Revenge* loose."

"Could you not even tell our position?" Uriah demanded.

The pilot hung his head. He knew he was forever disgraced and his profession lost.

"We are hung between two rocks," he confessed. "She will break up."

"All hands turn to make rafts," Uriah commanded.

# The Commodore

"We may have to float for it and take the cargo with us!" The government would forgive him the loss of his ship, for under the law and the fact, he had no responsibility, having the pilot on board and in charge. But he would never be forgiven if he failed to get the crew and the $48,000 he was carrying, safely ashore.

The terror of the remainder of that night was to haunt Uriah's dreams for years. The sea pounded harder and harder on the little vessel. The noise of the waves breaking on the reef and the ship's groaning as the hull scraped the rocks, added to the mingled prayers and curses of the crew, and the orders of the officers as they hurriedly lashed makeshift rafts.

When the sun came up over the sea, the hopeless position of the *Revenge* was immediately obvious. To leave her where she was, made her break-up certain. To drag her out from the rocks, even if possible, made sure that she would sink at once as the sea poured through the jagged holes in her hull!

Uriah calculated their position as forty miles from Belize and ordered the small boat put out again, with his junior lieutenant in command. With the help of a makeshift sail and a crew of oarsmen, the boat would have to try to reach Belize for assistance.

In a few hours a small pilot schooner hove in sight, and anchored in the quiet water within the reef, but it was impossible to get a boat to her, or to get a boat from the schooner to the *Revenge,* so great were the waves breaking about the war vessel.

Throughout that day Uriah drove the willing crew to finish the rafts, strip the vessel of everything of value, and haul the money sacks on deck where they might be taken off and saved, if ever it became possible to launch the rafts.

Early in the afternoon, there was a slight moderation in the sea and they were able to send off two of the rafts and reach the pilot boat with a line. After that they were pulled back and forth, hand over hand, while the crew transferred the sails, rigging, spars, clothes of the men and most of the provisions, to the pilot boat.

Uriah and all the remaining officers, and a fraction of the crew, together with the disgraced pilot who had been the cause of the misadventure, remained on board the *Revenge*.

For five miserable days they stayed aboard. The pilot boat had departed and there was no telling when the stripped down and battered hulk of the *Revenge* would pull clear of the rocks and sink.

There was nothing to be done but wait and hope for rescue. Uriah would not order the hulk abandoned while there was any chance whatsoever of salvage.

## 17

F IVE days is a long time to wait, with no telling at what moment the rafts might have to be launched and all hands sent off to try their luck with high seas, sharks, and other terrors of the tropical deep.

During those five days, all of Uriah's life to date seemed to parade across his consciousness. He was a boy again in staid, quiet Philadelphia, walking along the docks with Grandfather Phillips, wishing he could board one of the fine vessels he saw and venture out to sea. He was aboard the *New Jersualem,* listening to Captain Wilkins expounding the Bible. He was serving his apprenticeship to Mr. Coulter once more, and attending Talbot Hamilton's school during the days of the embargo. He could remember the voice of Hamilton and his English accent as he said, "Now once a qualified pilot has come aboard, in coastal waters, he is in command and the responsibility is his. The master of the ship does not give the orders then."

# The Commodore

Talbot Hamilton hadn't contemplated that the most eager pupil in his school would someday be stuck on a Honduras reef because of the incompetence of such a pilot!

Often during the five days, Uriah went back to the impressment and his escape from the British Navy; and most often of all to the long, long days on Dartmoor as a prisoner of war, with Princetown no more real a prison than was the *Revenge* at present, even though his jailer now was no Briton, but the sea.

Would it all end here, the ambition, the prayers, the quarrels, and the career? "What do I want of life," he asked himself, "if I live?" He had no doubt of the answer. "I wish to go on in the Navy, and in spite of the twin handicaps for that life of my religion and my having risen from the ranks, to serve myself best by serving my country. If I live," he vowed, "I will press on. Though blind chance seems to cheat me at every turn, yet I will persist. True, I missed the battle in which the *Argus* was lost; yes, I spent most of the war in a prison; admitted that only too lately Lafitte escaped me when the storm came up, and now I have lost my first naval command through no fault of my own. Yet, if I live, I will rise, and by my deeds make it easier for those who come after and would serve as I would serve!"

Often during those five days, he waxed philosophical. "Do you know, midshipman," he told one of the two youthful officers-to-be who was on the *Revenge*, "one thing this misfortune has proven to me beyond a doubt—it is not necessary to use the lash to make a crew behave. Show them only they must, and like all human beings, they'll do what they should. Not a man was in panic; not a man refused to do his duty."

"They were lashed by fear, sir, instead of the cat," the midshipman replied.

"Aye. But they can be lashed by ambition, as well."

At long last the five days of terror, of reverie, and of new resolution were ended by the arrival of a rescue vessel from Belize, sent out after the small boat from the *Revenge* had arrived to report the disaster. A crew of men well acquainted with the reef brought with them a chain cable, anchors, and a great ship's wrench capable of heaving with eight horsepower. The men brought word that the unhappy pilot would be tried by a colonial court of inquiry at Belize.

They went to work to salvage the *Revenge*. She was pulled, pushed, and twisted, but the poor hull could only shudder and moved from the rocks not a foot. Finally, the salvage crew was persuaded that nothing could be done, and told Uriah that he must abandon ship.

Now he ordered the recovery of the guns, which had been thrown overboard, and they were soon brought up and put aboard the salvage vessel. Even the masts were unstaffed and saved and at last there was nothing left whatever of the *Revenge* but the bare hull.

The money, the ship's papers, her flags, and the ship's instruments left the ship with the last of the crew. Uriah, as was his duty, was the last to leave the *Revenge*.

He looked back at the wreck sadly as the salvage vessel bore him off to Belize.

How ironical it was that he had succeeded in bringing his ship into Belize, a port he had never before seen, in

# The Commodore

the teeth of a hurricane, only to lose her through the carelessness or incompetence of a local pilot.

He wanted to say a prayer over the poor wreck, left so forlornly to the mercy of the seas. Was there a Hebrew prayer for dead ships, like the Kaddish for human beings? If there was, he didn't know it.

He turned away from the last view of his command and set his face resolutely toward Belize.

## ★ 18 ★

URIAH was able to charter a small schooner in Belize to take him, his crew, and the $48,000 he had saved from the wreck back to the United States.

He had expected to be criticized for the loss of the *Revenge,* but was surprised to find that Belize hailed him as a hero. The governor had sent for him and offered the apologies of the colonial government for the negligence of the pilot.

The manner in which Uriah had stayed on board his ship for five days and nights and had succeeded in saving everything but the bare hull, had won him the admiration of the maritime community. On arrival in Charleston, he found that letters from American sea captains in Belize had appeared in the Charleston newspapers, and the Navy, taking note of the spirit of Lieutenant Levy, was not critical.

He was ordered to rest at Charleston for a time, after

which it would be his turn to take shore duty. He was even told he might suggest his own assignment, and if a post suitable to his rank was open, he would be given it.

Uriah, having begun to learn French while in prison on Dartmoor, asked to be assigned to Paris for further study of that language. Such an assignment was a much sought after one for a bachelor in the service, and Uriah hardly dared hope it would come his way. But come it did, and in August of 1823, he was given six months leave for the purpose of studying in the French capital.

Paris in those days of the Bourbon restoration was beautiful and gay, and Uriah greatly enjoyed his stay. His leave was further extended, and it was nearly a year before he was ordered to report to the *U. S. S. Cyane,* then with the Mediterranean fleet at Leghorn, but soon to be shifted to the Brazil Squadron.

When Uriah joined the *Cyane,* he found a pleasanter attitude toward him than he had previously encountered on the other ships on which he had been stationed. He was no longer a junior lieutenant; his exploits as a merchant mariner in pursuing and capturing the piratical Tully and Dalton; his more recent voyage in the *Revenge* and his adventures in the War of 1812, had given his name a certain luster among his juniors.

Nevertheless, he did have a quarrel with a Lieutenant Spencer for the usual reasons, and was court-martialed once more, but this fifth court-martial of his career not only came out without damage to Uriah's own record, it also resulted in Lieutenant Spencer's suspension from the service for a year.

He was popular with most of the officers on the *Cyane.*

# The Commodore

The few who were prejudiced against him either because he had never been a midshipman, or because he had always been a Jew, feared him and put no difficulties in his way.

In 1827, while the *Cyane* was in the magnificent harbor of Rio de Janeiro, an incident occurred which finally won the hearts of the whole ship's company for Uriah.

It was necessary to repair the mainmast of the *Cyane*, so she was laid up in the yard of the Imperial Brazilian Navy.

At that time the Emperor, Dom Pedro, who came of the Portuguese royal house of Braganza, was on excellent terms with the United States. The facilities of Brazilian ports were open to the use of American war vessels, and the Emperor had been permitted to buy United States warships for use in his own Navy. One such vessel, a 60-gun frigate, had just arrived in Rio, and the great ship was an object of admiration to the Brazilian public.

However, the Brazilian Navy never had enough mariners to man its ships, and, as the British used to do, but no longer did, the Brazilians sometimes impressed foreign seamen into their Navy.

There was a midshipman by the name of Morris on the *Cyane*. He was proceeding through the Navy Yard, when a man in the uniform of the Brazilian Navy suddenly dashed out of a line of seamen and ran to Midshipman Morris.

"American," he gasped, "save me. Got drunk and when I woke up, I was shanghaied into the Brazilian Navy. I'm no Brazilian—I'm an American seaman. Save me, sir, save me!"

# The Commodore

The man spoke with a Yankee accent. Midshipman Morris said, "Any proofs, lad?"

"Yes—yes, seaman's papers."

By now, a squad of Brazilian sailors were approaching on the run.

"Follow me," the young Midshipman cried and set off speedily in the direction of the *Cyane's* dock.

The sailor ran beside him, but he could not keep up and Morris had to slow to a walk.

Two of the Brazilians had drawn bayonets from scabbards and now held the naked weapons in their hands like cutlasses.

Morris exclaimed, "We'll have to stand our ground, lad, and talk them out of it."

More Brazilians were now coming in every direction.

Uriah happened to be walking through the Navy Yard at that time, and hearing the commotion hastened to the scene. Recognizing Morris as a midshipman from the *Cyane,* he hurried toward him, but before he could reach his side, a Brazilian admiral, having also heard the noise, came rapidly toward the swelling and menacing crowd.

American sailors now came from the other direction. Uriah, seeing them, waved them back and called out, "Don't come until I give the order. Let me find out what is going on."

He hurried on and arrived at the scene of the controversy, just as the admiral did.

Uriah stood at the side of the midshipman and shouted, "What's the matter here?"

The midshipman replied, "American seaman, sir, escaping impressment."

"Impressment, eh," cried Uriah. "Then we'll save him."

At that moment, one of the sailors made a lunge for Morris with his bayonet. Uriah jumped at him and succeeded in deflecting the blow, but received it himself on the little finger of his right hand. At the same time, the second sailor with a bayonet struck at Uriah and tore a hole in his coat.

Uriah's hand bled profusely, but wrapping it quickly in his handkerchief, he fought with his fists. The Brazilian admiral now joined in the fracas, and the infuriated Morris leaped at him and knocked him down.

Uriah shouted an order and the Americans, who had armed themselves with sticks and stones, ran toward the melee. They were now equal in number to the Brazilians, and immediately the Americans charged into them, they ran, admiral and all, leaving Uriah, Morris and the seamen in the midst of their elated compatriots.

"Sir, you saved my life," gasped the midshipman.

"Nonsense. I'm just cut a little," replied Uriah, but blood was dripping from his handkerchief where he held it tightly around his hand, and a trickle of red came also from the side of his coat, where the bayonet had grazed him.

"Get this Yankee to the *Cyane*," Uriah ordered. Cheering, the American seamen picked up the escaped impressed sailor and carried him on their shoulders, on the run, to the safety of the American vessel.

Uriah's wounds were superficial, but he was the hero of the ship. He had saved a seaman from service in an alien navy, and the mariners would never forget him for that; and the junior officers would never cease to praise his quick action and dangerous self-exposure in assisting the midshipman.

Uriah expected a protest from the Brazilian admiral, but none was forthcoming.

The next day, Uriah had to carry his arm in a sling while he was engaged in charge of a gang of sailors in working on the mainmast ashore. He kept a sailor lookout stationed outside the shed in which he was working. He feared retaliation from the Brazilians and wanted to be warned of any sign of trouble approaching.

Uriah was in the shed for several hours and had almost forgotten that he had posted the lookout, when the man came on the run.

"Somebody big coming with a guard, sir," he reported. "Might be the admiral."

"Very well, we'll stand our ground, men, and see what happens."

But when the guards had marched in and stationed themselves on either side of the entrance to the shed, it was not the admiral who entered.

A whisper went about among the Americans. Their visitor was none other than Dom Pedro himself, the Emperor of Brazil!

Uriah had been presented to the Emperor before on one of the sovereign's previous visits to the shipyards. Uriah spoke no Portuguese, the language of Brazil and of the Emperor. Dom Pedro spoke no English, but as both he and Uriah were fluent in French, the Emperor had singled him out for special conversation.

Now Uriah, seeing the Emperor advancing, stepped

forward to meet him. Had the Emperor heard of the fracas of the day before and was he wrathful, Uriah wondered? Dom Pedro looked meaningly at the sling in which Uriah's hand was held, and then exclaimed.

"So, my French speaking Yankee Lieutenant, it was you who came to the rescue of your midshipman yesterday?"

A number of the officers with Uriah also understood French and in low tones translated the Emperor's remarks to their companions. All were very tense, for the Emperor's notice of the incident might be very serious for the future of Brazilian-American relations.

But the Emperor smiled and continued, "Allow me to congratulate you, Lieutenant, I have learned that you stepped into danger yesterday to rescue a common man— an ordinary seaman, of your nation. That was a brave and decent act on your part. I wish I had officers in our Navy who were as valorous and zealous as you are. I am happy that you succeeded, and have issued a stern order that no citizen of the United States is ever again to be impressed into our Navy."

Uriah smiled. "This is excellent news, Your Majesty," he exclaimed.

"I am sorry you were injured," Dom Pedro went on. "Have you a good surgeon aboard your ship? Otherwise, I shall be pleased to send my own to look after you."

A murmur of pleasure went around among the Americans as those who could understand translated for the others.

The Emperor continued, "I have come here for a purpose, Lieutenant. First, to offer an apology to you and the great nation you represent—"

"No apology is necessary, Your Majesty. Sailors would as soon fight as not. It is the nature of the calling."

"Nevertheless, we apologize. I have a further purpose. You have seen the 60-gun frigate, built in your country, which an American crew has just delivered to our Navy?"

"Certainly, sir, she is a beautiful ship, if I may say so."

"She is indeed, and we need fine sailors to sail her, and a brave captain to command her. Lieutenant, you are the man to command her. I am prepared to offer you the rank of captain in our Navy, second only to that of admiral, if you will enter the Brazilian service."

Uriah was dumbfounded, as were all those Americans who understood the Emperor. There were many foreign officers serving in the Brazilian Navy, but to offer the command of the largest ship in the fleet to a young American Lieutenant!

He stood looking at Dom Pedro, not sure that he had heard aright. He recalled that the man was not only the Emperor of Brazil, but a son of a King of Portugal. Three hundred years after the expulsion of the Jews from Portugal a scion of Portuguese royalty was offering him, Uriah Phillips Levy, a commission as captain in his Navy! What a sop to his vanity. A picture of himself paying an official visit to Philadelphia, sailing up the Delaware in command of the frigate—going to the Mikveh Israel on a Sabbath in the uniform of a captain of Brazil, flashed through his mind.

"You hesitate;" said Dom Pedro, pleasantly, "that is

natural—you need not make up your mind on the instant."

Uriah came back from his dreams. Hesitate? What did this foreign Emperor take him for?

"No, Your Majesty," he exclaimed, "I do not hesitate. I am indeed flattered by your kindness in making me this most magnificent offer. But I have no hesitation whatever. Your Majesty must graciously permit me to decline this great honor. You see, sir, I love my country and the Navy of the United States. I must tell you frankly, sir, and with no reflection upon you or your service—I would rather serve as a cabin boy in the United States Navy, than be admiral in any other service in the world."

When the other French speaking officers translated Uriah's words, there was a spontaneous cheer from all the Americans present. It died quickly, as the demonstrators remembered that they were on Brazilian soil and in the presence of the sovereign of that country. But the kindly look on the countenance of the Emperor reassured them.

"That sentiment does you honor, Lieutenant," he exclaimed. "It is my hope that there are some Brazilians who would answer as strongly if the offer were reversed. The Yankee Navy is the gainer and ours is the loser. I congratulate you, Lieutenant, on your constancy and patriotism. Both become you very well."

## 19

U RIAH had become extremely popular on the *Cyane.* His rescue of Midshipman Morris and the American seaman, and his declination of a captaincy and a fine command in the Brazilian Navy, made everyone look up to him as a hero. Those who had always liked him, now boasted of the fact. Those who had been inclined to prejudice against him, either because he had not served as a midshipman, or because he continued to practise the religion of his ancestors, now told each other that Levy was the exception who proved the rule.

Everyone was genuinely sorry when after more than two years' sea duty on the *Cyane,* Uriah received a routine transfer to shore duty.

In the peacetime Navy, most officers spent most of their lives on shore, at the various Navy Yards or on administrative assignments.

Because he had had so long a term of sea service aboard the *Cyane,* Uriah was given six months leave before being sent to his next post. He was now thirty-five years old. On his last trip to Paris he had been given State Department documents to deliver to the American Ambassador, and had also been ordered to observe the technical arrangements in English and French shipyards. He expected that his next post would be something along the same lines, probably in Europe, for his mastery of the French language would qualify him above the ordinary, for such duty.

He did not know it—he would have been horrified to know it—but he had seen his last sea duty for eleven years.

During his leave, having accumulated a modest sum of money from his pay and allowances, he called on Mr. John Coulter, his old master and employer. Coulter was now a highly prosperous merchant, with ships sailing on many seas to many ports.

Coulter was glad to see Uriah.

"Heard much of you," he told him. "I never doubted you would be a hero. But where is it leading, Uriah? You are still comparatively young—why don't you leave the Navy, marry, settle down here in Philadelphia, and come into my business? Your experiences in the Navy will be valuable to me. In no time you can be well off. I saw your mother lately. She is aging and failing rapidly. Why not delight her old age by leading a good life ashore, here in Philadelphia?"

"You are very kind," exclaimed Uriah. "Sometimes I fancy I would like to marry, but I feel married to the sea—and she is a jealous wife."

"But have you never been in love with a woman, Uriah?"

# The Commodore

"I am almost always in love with somebody or other," he confessed. "Once, very seriously. It was in Paris, when I was twenty-seven," he reminisced. "The lady was French and noble—the daughter of a Marquis. It pains me even now to remember—I have never spoken of it to any other American—"

"Indeed? Why does it pain you, Uriah?"

"It provoked a conflict within me. I do not like such conflicts. We were deeply in love for two years."

"Was there an obstacle to a marriage?"

"None—except ourselves. At first, she professed to find it impossible to contemplate life in America, even though she loved me so much."

"And then?"

"As long as she would not come, I was in no danger. But at last she began to change. She seriously considered marriage and departure for Philadelphia. Then, I found it impossible."

"But why, Uriah? Many European ladies have married Americans and have been very happy here."

"The fault was mine, not hers, if it was a fault," Uriah explained. "You see, she was not of my faith."

"And this alone kept you from the marriage?" asked John Coulter.

"Yes," Uriah confessed. "Oh, I know many who have as we put it, 'married out'—and some have been happy, in spite of the difference in background—but you see, Mr. Coulter, I have set out to have a career which will not compromise. I mean for all time. I hope when a young Jew considers whether or not he should seek a naval career, he will say to himself, "That I shall! Look at Uriah Levy and what he did—and that without pretending in any way to be anything but what he was."

"And what has this to do with your marriage to a French noblewoman?" inquired John Coulter.

"Had I done this, then when those to come thought of me, they might have said, 'Yes, he was born a Jew, but he didn't practise his faith; he married out, you know.' "

"Your faith requires you to marry one of your own faith?"

"Yes. Not from snobbishness, but to preserve our way of life—especially the warmth of our family life, which I do believe is superior to any I have observed. I believe it is largely our ban on intermarriage which has resulted in our faith continuing in a hostile world through two millenniums."

"So you gave up love so that others might find in you a sterling example."

Uriah laughed. "Perhaps I give myself too much credit. Perhaps I also fled responsibility. Perhaps I didn't wish to offend my mother—she would be deeply offended if I 'married out,' feeling it was a reflection on her. But I truly believe it was because I mean to have a place in history, and therefore, I shall be consistent—a Jew to the utmost.

"Now, my friend, you have heard a confession I have never made to anyone before, and now I must give you the same answer I gave to Dom Pedro of Brazil. My mother has plenty of my brothers and sisters here at home to comfort her. I would not and could not give up the naval career. Why, Mr. Coulter, I am well on my way."

"Way to what, my son?"

# The Commodore

"I do not know exactly, but I am in the right life for me—of this I am sure. But there is a matter about which I came to you, sir. I have a little money put by and would like to invest it with you. I have seen a great deal of merchant shipping and learned a great deal, I think, from what I have seen. Perhaps while I am home on leave, we could talk over my ideas, and if you see fit to follow them, you could use my money—"

"Very good, Uriah."

A sort of partnership came to be, with Uriah a silent participant. It was to continue for a decade, during which Uriah's original stake was greatly increased by the prudence of John Coulter, as well as by Uriah's own profitable ideas, for the development of water-borne trade and for the economical management of merchant ships.

He also purchased various parcels of real estate in New York, and became so enthusiastic about the life and growth of that city that he changed his residence, when ashore, to that city, joining Shearith Israel Congregation, but continuing to spend much time in his mother's residence in Philadelpha. His mother was growing very old. She was proud of her children, but never quite realized they were grown to manhood and womanhood. One of Uriah's younger brothers, Jonas Phillips Levy, had also begun a naval career.

"I suppose you will retire from the Navy when you are a rich man," John Coulter once teased him.

"Certainly not. I will use the money for a better purpose. Among other uses, I mean to use it for the glory of my country. For example, I consider Thomas Jefferson one of the greatest men in history. Think of it—author of *The Declaration*—and an absolute democrat, sir, in every way. Yet there is no statue to him in the Capitol in Washington."

"I do not follow," exclaimed the bewildered Coulter. "What has that to do with you, Uriah?"

"Much. Jefferson should serve as an inspiration to millions of Americans yet unborn. I mean to help in that, as small repayment for his determined stand on the side of religious liberty, which did much to mold our young Republic in a form in which a man's religion did not make him ineligible for political or governmental life. Why, sir, when I have enough money, I shall personally commission a statue of Jefferson for the Capitol in Washington."

"You are an odd one, Uriah. Do you feel that one man like you must go about doing what the public has neglected to do? That is worthy of a Don Quixote."

"I don't care for money for itself," said Uriah stubbornly. "It is wrong that a great nation should neglect its heroes. Therefore, when I am able, I am going to do my little part by buying the statue."

"Too bad you couldn't help your hero while he was alive. His friends had to pay his debts."

"I know that—unfortunately, at that time, I had no money. I hear his beautiful home at Monticello is going to ruin. How ungrateful is the Republic! If I had the money, I would buy the place and preserve it—" Uriah spoke very vehemently as always.

How strange was this man whose character had so many sides, thought John Coulter. Was it a form of vanity which made him wish to be a public benefactor, or was it a genuine, all-consuming desire to see to it that the Republic's heroes should not go unremembered? Perhaps many a sailor, in the battle's peril in wartime, thinks "Do I do all this for those who stay at home?" And feels, too, "If they remember me for it, it was good." But to be a hero and forgotten—wouldn't that seem the worst fate to a man of Uriah's dashing patriotism?

Well, Uriah should do what he liked with his money, John Coulter thought, but as for himself, he would rather put back the profit into more good sturdy ships to carry more and more cargo to the greater glory—and wealth— of John Coulter.

At the scheduled end of his leave, Uriah was pleased to be permitted to extend it, and to go to Paris once more to study and observe on behalf of the Navy.

As soon as he arrived there, he decided he was already wealthy enough to order the statue of Jefferson, and on learning from the government that such a statue would be acceptable, he commissioned the great Pierre David, one of the most famous sculptors of his day, to make the statue.

Uriah was by now quite well known in Paris. On one of his previous visits he had secured a letter of introduction from William Crawford, the American Minister to France, who had been taken with the young Uriah on his crossing on the *Argus* so many years ago, to the aged General Lafayette himself.

Uriah had called on the famous friend and aide of Washington, and the old Marquis had received him kindly.

Uriah had been delighted. The old patriot was an in-

teresting conversationalist. When he had learned of the
fact that Washington had come to Uriah's Aunt Zipporah's wedding, he had regaled Uriah with anecdotes
of the first President; and when the American went on
to tell him about his admiration for Thomas Jefferson,
Lafayette told him how he, too, had admired the great
Virginian and how sad it had made him to learn that
Jefferson had died in debt.

"That beautiful house he built—Monticello, it was
called, was it not? I wonder what has become of it?"
asked Lafayette.

"I do not know, General," replied Uriah, but he was
determined to find out when next he was in America. "I
have heard rumors that it is in decay. The homes of great
men should be preserved as monuments to their glory,"
he exclaimed.

"You are right," said Lafayette sadly—"But in France
we have too many such monuments. Sometimes the dead
weigh down the living."

Now he called on the Marquis again. He told him of
the commissioning of the statue of Jefferson, and of the
lamentable fact he had confirmed that Monticello was
falling into ruins.

"Someday, if my fortunes prosper, I shall do something about that," he promised Lafayette, "but for now,
I am using all the profit from my ventures with Mr.
Coulter to commission the great David to make the
statue. It shall stand in the Capitol in Washington so
that each day, as the lawmakers pass, they may reflect on
the tolerance, the patriotism, and the wisdom of Thomas
Jefferson."

# The Commodore

Lafayette praised the gesture and offered to lend his painting of Jefferson by Sully to serve as David's model.

Then he asked if Uriah was attending the banquet celebrating the Fourth of July in Paris.

"Most certainly, sir, and I understand you will grace the table with your presence."

Lafayette nodded. Who more than the old friend of Washington, Uriah thought, deserved better to sit at the seat of honor there!

The Fourth of July banquet was attended by every American of any consequence who was in Paris.

After the meal, a prominent American visitor rose and proposed a toast to the memory of Washington. As they stood to drink, the celebrants saw a tear run down the face of the aged Marquis de Lafayette.

There followed a toast to "The King of the French— His Majesty Charles X." Someone shouted, approvingly, "Nine cheers and one more," and the entire assemblage complimented the French who were present by cheering ten times and then drinking the health of their sovereign.

Thereafter, another American rose and proposed a toast to "Andrew Jackson, President of the United States; like Washington, firm and patriotic; like Washington, happy in the union of men and principles."

Instantly Uriah was on his feet. "I propose nine cheers," he shouted, wishing to be the first to second the toast to the American President. He was astounded by the reaction. He had forgotten that "Old Hickory," the plain man in the White House, was not popular with Frenchmen, and indeed very unpopular with the type of American who considered himself an aristocrat. When

# The Commodore

Uriah proposed nine cheers, a great hissing and booing swept the room.

Uriah was livid, as was the proposer of the toast. Uriah cried, "We are toasting the President of the United States, not the man, and I insist you cease this outrage. When you hiss the toast, you insult the United States of America, whose Chief Magistrate is Andrew Jackson."

Everyone was quiet except for a few who were intoxicated and laughed gaily. When quiet was restored, Uriah exclaimed, "Now once more I second the toast and call for nine cheers."

Many of the Americans present, ashamed of refusing to cheer their own President, before foreigners, now joined in the cheers, but some of the Frenchmen did not. One in particular, who sat directly across the table from Uriah, hissed and booed loudly during the cheering. Uriah regarded him, then turned to a gentleman sitting next him and said, "Who is that man?"

"That is Monsieur Bayeux, the most wealthy glove merchant in France," replied Uriah's neighbor, in a low voice.

"A glove merchant, is he," exclaimed Uriah. He pulled one of his own gloves from his pocket and flung it full in the Frenchman's face.

"That, sir," proclaimed Uriah, "is not an order for a case of gloves, but an invitation to meet me in the Champs Elysées tomorrow morning at dawn. Name your second, sir, and I shall name mine, and we shall see tomorrow whether or not you can insult the United States of America on the glorious Fourth of July—aye, and in the presence of the noblest Frenchman who ever took up his sword for liberty."

# The Commodore

Monsieur Bayeux turned pale. He rose and left the room and some of the other Frenchmen followed him. Others crowded around Uriah, apologizing for the discourtesy of their countryman.

Those Americans who were pro-Jackson also thronged around Uriah and shook his hand. Even those Americans who were anti-Jackson, realizing that Uriah's point was well taken, though still resenting the comparison of Jackson with Washington, quietly told each other that the fiery Levy had courage.

At length General Lafayette himself approached Uriah.

"Sir," he said, "that man did not speak for France. I am glad you did not allow him to insult your President."

Uriah was proud but he was also a little ashamed of himself. Hadn't he promised himself never to be involved in another duel? Wasn't it bad enough to remember how he had killed Potter, under the dueling oaks in New Jersey? What would the Navy say to all this?

A few hours later, he was able to smile again. A messenger brought a note to his apartment. It was an apology from Monsieur Bayeux. He hoped the honor of the American could be assuaged by the written apology, and there need be no duel!

"Tell him I accept his apology," Uriah told the messenger. "But tell him the next time he goes to an American celebration he had better cheer very loudly when the President is toasted, if I am present."

## 20

AT LENGTH Pierre David, the sculptor, had finished the heroic size statue of Jefferson and it was shipped off to America, where, upon arrival in the port of Norfolk, it was drawn in a wagon hauled by oxen all the way to Washington and set up in the Capitol. Uriah gave the original clay model for the statue to the City of New York, which city he had come to consider his home.

On his arrival back in the United States, he was pleased when he found his simple act of homage to the dead President had touched the spirit of the American people. Levy was praised on all sides, and the City of New York delighted him when the Mayor, Cornelius Lawrence, in a public ceremony, presented him with a gold box on which was inscribed a tribute to Uriah's "character, patriotism and public spirit."

During his leave in the United States, Uriah had occasion to go to Philadelphia to confer with John Coulter, and he could not resist taking the gold box with him and exhibiting it to his old friends at Mikveh Israel before the Sabbath service.

"It makes me feel I have come a long way from the little boy who haunted the docks here," he told his brothers and sisters.

He was happy, too, that his younger brother, Jonas Phillips Levy was following in Uriah's footsteps. Jonas was now a junior lieutenant in the naval service.

On the visit to his native city, he showed the box to his brother and told him, "You will not find it easy to be a Jew and an officer, but if you only remember that you need three qualities, besides seamanship and capacity to lead—I mean patriotism, valor, and fidelity, you will rise in the service."

Soon after this conversation, Uriah himself rose, for he was promoted to Commander. His commission was signed by Andrew Jackson. Jackson had heard of Uriah's fiery effort on the President's behalf when the diners in Paris had refused to drink his health, and "Old Hickory" smiled with satisfaction as he followed the Navy's recommendation and raised the rank of his defender.

In his new rank, which would give him command of one of the largest ships in the Navy, he looked forward eagerly to his return to sea duty.

Meanwhile, his personal affairs continued to prosper and he found himself able to purchase the rundown but still beautiful estate of Monticello, in Virginia. Now he was master of the residence of his idol.

He went to Virginia and strolled about the 218-acre

estate, for which he had paid only twenty-seven hundred dollars. How sad it was to think of the care which Thomas Jefferson had lavished on his home, only to have it become this rundown, decrepit and decaying plantation.

"I shall put every penny I have, or shall have, in restoring the place as a worthy monument to the great man who designed and built it," he vowed.

He induced his mother to come down and visit the house.

"Is it seemly," old Rachel asked, "for an old nobody like me to walk the halls where President Jefferson once dwelt?"

"It is, indeed, Mamma," said her son. "What is not seemly is for my mother to stay in such a rundown mansion. We shall soon remedy that."

Whenever he could, Uriah returned to Virginia to superintend the restoration of the estate, and his profits from his shipping ventures and his New York real estate speculations were put into the redevelopment of Monticello.

Yet all he did, busy though it kept him, journeying back and forth between Philadelphia, New York and Virginia, with occasional trips to London and Paris, did not in Uriah's view compensate him for leading a life ashore instead of the sea duty which it was his passionate desire to have.

In 1838, Commander Uriah Levy was suddenly made supremely happy by receiving orders to report at once to Pensacola, Florida, there to take command of the *U. S. S. Vandalia,* one of the largest sloops then in active service.

# The Commodore

This was no gunboat *Revenge;* this was a ship of the line and Uriah's great ambition as a naval officer was to command such a vessel.

He set off posthaste for Florida, and on September 12, 1838, arrived at Pensacola and joined his ship. He was full of ideas for the conduct of his command. For eleven years he had dreamed of this day. He would demonstrate to the world that an American ship-of-war could be well sailed by an American crew without the use of the lash; he would show that Jeffersonian democracy could be used aship as well as ashore; there were a thousand and one innovations he hoped to make, so that he might be remembered as a progressive and inventive officer as well as an efficient one.

He felt he would never forget his disillusionment as he stepped aboard his command for the first time to receive the salutes of his juniors.

The day was very warm, but Uriah was spruce in his newest uniform. The *Vandalia* had been at sea, chiefly in the Caribbean for three years without a real overhaul or a change of crew. Her bottom was foul with barnacles, her canvas was old and worn, and her crew discouraged.

When Commander Levy came aboard and saluted the flag flying on what was to be his ship, only a single officer, one of the four lieutenants in the ship's complement, returned his salute.

"Where are the others?"

"Ashore in Pensacola."

"And the midshipmen?" (of whom there were five).

"Also ashore, sir, we did not expect you today."

"Send after them at once."

# The Commodore

"Aye, aye, sir."

Uriah soon found the reason for the lack of officers aboard. Discipline was very lax and three of his four lieutenants were alcoholics!

No sooner was the *Vandalia* at sea, bound for the West Indies, than one of his lieutenants, who was in a drunken stupor, fell overboard and was drowned, and a second went out of his mind from drink, and had to be locked up for the voyage.

Uriah promoted his sailing master and a midshipman to acting lieutenants and sailed on. He had been waiting many years for this command, and during the years of waiting, he had brooded over methods of improving discipline on the ships of the Navy. He remembered that the *Argus* had probably been lost because of the drunkenness of the crew, and many another good ship as well.

Very well. Uriah would show the world—and the Navy—that even such a crew as he had on the *Vandalia* could be disciplined without the cat-o'-nine tails.

He posted an order—"When any man returns on board ship in a state of intoxication, all officers are ordered to keep away from and not exchange a word with him. His messmates are to take charge of and lead him forward and lash him up in his hammock—but if necessary, he will be put in irons or confined by order of the Captain."

He issued another. A man who had been drunk need not be beaten; instead he would wear a wooden bottle, marked "Drunk," suspended from a string around his neck for a day or two.

Was it reported to him that petty thievery was rampant on board the *Vandalia*? Uriah ordered that if a man was caught as a thief, instead of being given twelve lashes with the cat, as heretofore, he should wear a wooden collar, marked "Thief," for three days.

As for the midshipmen, those intending officers should be taught more than "navigation and strong drink," as it was sometimes said facetiously, denoted their course of study.

"Midshipmen will be taught the elements of seamanship," Uriah explained. "It does not do to have officers who cannot do everything an able seaman can do. They shall learn gunnery, the repair of a ship, and how to handle the oars."

The midshipmen grumbled when Uriah made them row themselves ashore, instead of having members of the crew do it for them. One day, in a West Indian port when Uriah sent three midshipmen ashore in a small boat, and sent two of the ship's boys to sit in the stern, and after the midshipmen were ashore, to row the small boat back to the *Vandalia,* the outraged midshipmen filed a formal protest to the Commodore of the West Indies fleet and the Commodore peremptorily ordered Uriah to cease from pursuing the innovation. It would lessen the respect of the crew for the midshipmen, their future officers, if they saw the midshipmen rowing!

The Commodore also cautioned Uriah against the abolition of the cat-o'-nine tails. Uriah prudently did not make any such formal order—instead, he invented other disciplinary measures so that the lash was seldom called upon to correct an unruly seaman. If a man fought on deck, as the crewmen were sometimes apt to do, he

was given a pot of sea water and commanded to drink
it to "cool his hot blood."

Those of the officers and crew who were not too far
gone with alcoholism soon responded to the new regime
and Uriah's theories were vindicated when the *Vandalia*,
in spite of her age and lack of overhaul, became known
through the West Indies fleet as a well-sailed, well-disciplined ship, whose officers and crew could be depended
on to execute any mission.

In spite of the doubts of the Commodore, Uriah was
a proud and happy commander. He had proved his
methods worked.

He was especially proud when, because of the good
state of discipline and seamanship on the *Vandalia*, she
was ordered on a dangerous and difficult voyage in Mexican waters.

## 21

MEXICO was in a turbulent condition. The central government had very little control over the states, and from time to time adventurous generals attempted to take over various local governments and form combinations against the federal authority.

Only a year before, a French fleet had bombarded Vera Cruz when a local authority refused to pay a debt alleged to be due a French company. Anti-foreign, and especially anti-American feeling was high. American consuls, in pursuit of their official duties, were often insulted and prevented from going about their legitimate business.

Uriah was ordered to take the *Vandalia* to Mexican waters, to make a series of calls on American consuls stationed there, and later on, when the seasonal winds permitted, to call at Yucatan and investigate a reported insult to the American consul there.

It was a mission to delight his heart. Alone and in

# The Commodore

command, he would show the flag he loved in a hostile foreign land and exact respect for the principles for which the flag stood.

He headed first for the mouth of the Rio Grande, where the consul at Matamoras, many miles inland, had reported that he and all Americans in the town were in urgent danger. Arrived at the mouth of the river, Uriah was unable to ascend it in the *Vandalia* because a sand bar blocked the river's mouth.

"We'll go up in a small-boat," he decided. He put a boat overside and rowed by members of his crew, went up river twenty-eight miles, to put in a sudden appearance in the town which astonished the Mexicans and delighted the Americans.

With an armed guard of sailors from the *Vandalia,* Uriah escorted the American consul to the local governor and extracted apologies from him and promises of protection for Americans in the vicinity.

Uriah's next port of call was Tampico. Here it was possible to bring the *Vandalia* into gunshot distance of the hot, dismal tropical port. Again Uriah went ashore, and helped the consul to assert the rights of American citizens in the anarchy which then prevailed in Mexico's Gulf ports.

Between calls ashore, he frequently stopped and searched vessels suspected to be slavers or piratical ships.

Day after day went by in this manner, cruising in the Gulf. Each day was much like the day before, except for Sundays. On Sundays, Uriah was especially mindful of the religious sensibilities of the crew. Being Jewish, he wished to be more than scrupulous in his respect for the religion of the sailors. Each morning and evening he said his own Hebrew prayers in the privacy of his cabin, but on Sundays, he would have the ship's bell sound a church call and all sailors not on watch were called to the quarterdeck, where a hymn would be sung. Uriah would then read a chapter of the Old Testament, after which one of his lieutenants would read a chapter of the New. All hands, except the commander, were excused from unnecessary work on Sunday. Uriah, himself, on his own part, avoided all unnecessary activity on his own Sabbath.

One Saturday, however, he had no choice but to act, and act quickly.

A French frigate of war was cruising in the Gulf. Uriah decided to come in for anchorage in a small Mexican harbor, and the French vessel came in parallel to the *Vandalia*, also seeking a berth. A sudden shift in the wind caused the two vessels to come dangerously close to each other. The rigging of the two ships caught, and only by skillful maneuvering on Uriah's part was a collision averted. Some tackle from the French sails fell to the deck of the French ship, and immediately the French commander rushed to the rail nearest the *Vandalia*, shook his fist at the lieutenant of the watch, and shouted gross and obscene insults to the American.

The two vessels pulled apart undamaged, but Uriah, who had well understood the French commander's remarks, was livid with rage. What right had French ships in Mexican waters, anyhow? Hadn't they ever heard of the Monroe Doctrine?

# The Commodore

"Lucky for you," Uriah shouted, "that the *Vandalia* wasn't nearby when you and your kind bombarded Vera Cruz."

As soon as the *Vandalia* had found safe anchorage, and he had heard the anchor chain of the French ship go down, Uriah ordered a small-boat put over, and proceeded to have himself rowed to hailing distance of the French vessel.

Then he stood in the bow and shouted, in his best French, "I am Commander Levy, of the United States Navy. Tell your captain that I understood his remarks and consider them an insult to my ship and flag. If he does not apologize at once, I shall call him out to settle the affair with me. Tell him the last Frenchman who insulted my government was called out by me in Paris, and apologized."

Uriah looked around at the sailors in his own boat. He translated what he had said for their benefit, and a cheer went up.

"May the Lord forgive me for making such threats on the Hebrew Sabbath day," he exclaimed in English. "But I believe I shall be forgiven, for the honor of our country is insulted."

There was a short period of great activity on the French ship, as the officer of the watch went below to report the American's remarks to his commander.

Then the French captain appeared on his quarterdeck. He observed the size of the *Vandalia,* and the businesslike guns which showed from their ports—and which Uriah, as one more innovation, had caused to be painted

# The Commodore

blue, which made them even more startling and formidable than the usual dark black of the gun metal—and then the French captain called, in English.

"A 'tousand pardons, Monsieur, for ze remark I 'ave made. I meant no offense to you or your government."

Another cheer went up from the American crew. By golly, their skipper might be odd in some ways, but he knew how to put the foreigner in his place!

"Your apology is accepted," shouted Uriah, also in English. "I shall report the incident to my government, but state that you made a proper apology."

Then he ordered the small-boat back to the *Vandalia* and resumed his sabbath rest.

When Uriah put in at Vera Cruz, three days later, the French ship had already called there, and word had spread through the towns that the commander of the *Vandalia* was a fire-eater. The Mexican authorities were most respectful, and the American consul jubilant when he was permitted to send away a large sum belonging to American interests in care of Commander Levy.

Uriah was happier than he had ever been in his life. He was showing the flag in the protection of American life and property; he was demonstrating that discipline on an American ship need not be enforced by the whip; he was sailing the seas as master of a great ship.

When it became necessary to wait for favorable winds to venture into the coastal waters of Yucatan, he and his two officers went exploring up a Mexican river in a small-boat. Uriah's naturally boundless curiosity drew him to collect specimens of plant and animal life and bring them back for the inspection of scientists at home.

# The Commodore

He also spent much time in revising naval charts of the waters in which he was sailing, finding them often faulty.

At length, when the winds turned in April, Uriah turned the *Vandalia* to the south again and made for the Yucatan, the isolated hotbed of the Mexican troubles. Here real difficulties were to be expected, for there were no harbors, the waters were sometimes shallow, and the Indians and the politicians ashore were both sure to be hostile. But there was glory in the voyage. Exulting, Uriah redoubled his effort to better the seamanship and discipline of the crew.

He was pleased that since he had been in Mexican waters, not once had the cat-o'-nine tails had to be called into use to correct an erring seaman. It was true that at Vera Cruz, after a shore liberty, quite a few wooden bottles had been hung about the necks of seamen, and for one ship's boy of sixteen, who had mimicked the manners of the ship's officers, a new and unusual punishment had to be invented to save his back from the customary lash marks. Uriah had the boy tied to a gun as though to be lashed, but instead, he caused to be applied a small quantity of tar—about the size of a silver dollar, to the boy's bare back, and to the tar were stuck about a dozen brilliant parrot's feathers, the parrot being a bird who often mimicked his betters. The boy was very much humiliated, and was promptly cured of his disposition to mimic, but it did not harm him nearly as much, Uriah was sure, as twelve lashes would have done.

With a well-disciplined crew, therefore, and a spruce, if weatherbeaten ship, Uriah came to anchor fifteen miles off-shore from the little town of Laguna de Termines, the

# The Commodore

closest in he could get to that shallow line of shore to which his mission had brought him.

The next morning, he came in to the beach in the small-boat, not knowing what to expect, and with his armed guard from the *Vandalia* well instructed in battle duties in the event that shooting started.

He was received by the seedy-looking Captain of the Port with great suspicion, but on Uriah's imperious insistence, he sent a messenger for the American consul while Uriah waited at the beach, his party drawn up in full array.

In about a half hour, the perspiring consul arrived. "Mighty glad to greet you, Commander. Nobody ever looked better to me than you," said the Honorable Jack Thomas, U. S. Consul in the Yucatan. "The State Department kind of forgets about me from time to time, and this time it has been for a whole year. I sent 'em a message lately that things are very bad here."

"They are bad all along the gulf coast, Mr. Thomas. You know how they dislike us—and in the present state of anarchy, every little general tries to become popular by baiting the Yankee."

Uriah went on to tell of his experiences at Matamoras, Tampico and Vera Cruz.

The consul invited him to his house, and Uriah paraded his guard behind an American flag through the ragged, dirty streets of the little town, to the astonishment of the loungers before the cantinas, who believed an American invasion was occurring. No one offered any resistance.

The consul then took Uriah to call upon the civil

and military authorities—who consisted of a cadaverous looking old mayor, who was suffering from ague and shook constantly while he bade Uriah welcome—and a fat, half-breed Indian general, who said polite words, but spat at Uriah's feet at the end of each sentence. The general waved a palm leaf fan before his face constantly, hiding his unease with the endless motion.

Briefly, the consul told the general that he had insulted the United States government on a number of occasions when he had taken money and valuables from American citizens, failed to keep order in the country, and refused to listen to his, Jack Thomas', consul of the United States, protests.

"Now, Commander Levy is here to secure your apologies and restitution of the valuables stolen. His ship, a great vessel of war, is anchored off your coast. If he does not get satisfaction, he will sail close in and bombard the town. Also, he requires an agreement of friendship to be signed, whereby my rights as consul, will be respected. I am a man of patience, general, but Commander Levy is not. Perhaps you have heard of him before, and how he chased pirates and slavers off the sea. Now he is prepared to chase generals—but he is also ready to shake your hand in friendship if you will do the right thing."

The general's fan waved vigorously, while he considered the ultimatum.

He said, "We Mexicans are many. The American officer has but few. He should not come here to our country."

"He would not have come, general, if you had treated Americans with respect. We don't care a continental how you treat Mexicans, but you're going to treat me and all Americans with respect or face trouble."

The fan went again. Then the general said, "I robbed no one. I will give friendship, but I cannot return what I do not have."

"You must get it back—all of it," exclaimed Uriah. "That will be the task of your army. My terms are as follows—Return of everything to the rightful owners. A promise to treat our consul with respect. No treachery by either side, on penalty of my return to blow your town to bits. A salute to our flag by a squad of your troops."

Again the fan waved.

Then the general said, calmly, "All this can be. In return I must have medicine from your ship—my men are sick with fever. Also, a new uniform, like the one you are wearing. Also, two barrels of American whiskey. Also, if I salute the Yankee flag, the Yankee must salute my flag. Agreed?"

"Agreed," said Uriah, "except we have only one barrel of whiskey on board. I'll give you a uniform of my own, minus the insignia, and promise you the other barrel of whiskey by the next American warship to come along the coast."

"There will be another?"

"Of course, to see that you have kept your promise to the consul. If you have—we will throw in two more barrels of whiskey and a brass telescope to let you look five miles out to sea. If you haven't—we will blow your town to bits and destroy your army."

The next day, the grateful consul and Uriah stood at attention while a raggle-taggle army of barefoot soldiers paraded before them and saluted the American flag, after which, the American sailors saluted the tattered banner of the general.

Now that all was settled, the general was very friendly, said that Uriah was "muy valiente—muy simpático" and drank his health.

Before Uriah left two days later, almost all the loot had been returned to the American owners, and the entire American colony—about a dozen strong—gave Uriah a testimonial letter of thanks.

Proudly Uriah sailed away from Yucatan. Now he had sailed the whole Gulf coast of Mexico and his mission was accomplished, he set sail for Pensacola. He had been on a long cruise and it was time the *Vandalia* was laid up, and her crew given a long period ashore in the United States. Uriah himself would probably go back to shore duties, or on leave awaiting orders, for the number of commanders in the Navy was many more than the available peacetime assignments.

On the way home he conscientiously stopped a dozen vessels of suspicious appearance, looking for slaves, but was pleased when he encountered no ship which was not engaged in legitimate commerce.

He sailed into Pensacola proudly and happily, his duty well done.

What was his astonishment to find on arrival, that although his exploits were praised in the American press and his humanity in his treatment of his crew commended, the Navy thought otherwise!

What, said the old martinets in the service, jealous of their right to soundly flog a sailor who dared break a

# The Commodore

rule, put a bit of tar and some parrot's feathers on a ship's boy's back? Inhuman! Court-martial for the commander who dared to order such cruelty!

Uriah couldn't believe it—yet when he remembered his five previous court-martials, for reasons often as trivial—he knew that it was true.

He returned to his beloved Monticello and awaited the inevitable proceedings. What did he care—the public, the press, the people—and the seamen—looked up to him.

The court-martial was held and Uriah was found guilty! The Board sentenced him to dismissal from the Navy, but President John Tyler, finding the sentence preposterous, reduced it to suspension for one year without pay.

"Well," said Uriah, "ever since Roman days, Republics have not been overwhelming in their gratitude. But it was not the Republic, but a few old officers, who cannot yet forget that I was never a midshipman and am always a Jew—even to my Jewish attitude of charity to the wrongdoer—who are ungracious. What need I care—I shall commune with the shades of the great Thomas Jefferson for a year upon the lawns of Monticello, and then return refreshed to the fray."

## 22

RIAH did not know it, but it was to be eighteen years before he again saw active service aboard a ship of war. At the end of his year of suspension, he was told to await orders. Two years later, he was promoted to captain—the highest rank in the Navy, there being no admiral in the United States Navy before the Civil War. The officer who commanded a fleet was a commodore while in command, and by courtesy after such command. But in the Navy rolls, a commodore, not in active service, was a captain.

At the time of Uriah's promotion to captain, at the age of 50, he was one of the youngest officers to reach that rank, the average age of captains at that time being 59.

But holding the rank of captain did not automatically give Uriah a command. He begged for active service, but somehow, it was never forthcoming. Sixteen times during the years he was awaiting orders, he wrote to the Navy asking for service, but the Navy never called him.

In 1848, when the Mexican War broke out, he wrote to the Secretary of the Navy. Surely one with so much knowledge of the gulf waters would be useful. He reminded the Secretary "My term of life may be short, and this will be the only opportunity which will offer when I will be fit to serve my country in a state of war," but he was given no duty.

He offered to command a ship carrying grain to sufferers from a famine in Ireland—he even asked for command of the Philadelphia Navy Yard, though greatly preferring sea duty—but each time he was given no command.

He was far from idle, however, and never depressed. He spent his winters in New York, where his investments in real estate proved very profitable as the growth of the metropolis increased land values. He visited Philadelphia frequently, on affairs connected with the shipping business, which also prospered. He spent the months from April to October at Monticello.

He was happiest during the season of his visits to the Virginia estate. He worked much in the garden, and with his own hands helped in the restoration of the beautiful house which Jefferson had designed. There was not much left of the elaborate furnishings. A bust of Voltaire, which had belonged to Jefferson; and a column designed by Jefferson to add an American capital to the classic Greek styles of Doric, Ionic and Corinthian, stood in the great hall. Jefferson had designed the leaves of the capital to resemble corn, a characteristically American plant, instead of the lotus of the Egyptian.

Uriah also had Jefferson's great clock, showing the days of the week and other calendarial information, and the gig for travelling which the third President had built for himself.

The remaining furnishings were largely Uriah's own. John Coulter, his former master from Philadelphia, now a very old man, came to Monticello to visit Uriah. Uriah took Coulter to see his own mother's grave, where Rachel Levy lay in the red, Virginia earth. Then he took him to see Thomas Jefferson's grave, also on the grounds of Monticello.

"See what has happened to the monument," Uriah pointed out as they looked at the crumbling obelisk which marked the President's grave. "Tourists have chipped it away piece by piece, so that they might put a stone or two in their curio cabinets labelled, 'From T. Jefferson's grave.' Barbarous, eh, Mr. Coulter?"

"It is indeed, Uriah. Why do you let them come?"

"I consider myself only a temporary tenant," exclaimed Uriah. "Monticello will always belong to Thomas Jefferson alone, no matter who is the nominal legal owner. This place should be for the whole nation, and some day it will be. At my death, by will, I am giving it to the people of the United States, Mr. Coulter."

"That's a noble thought, Uriah. I hope it is more promptly accepted by the Congress than your statue by David."

Uriah laughed, "Congress is slow moving, but what do I care, the statue is in the Capitol where it belongs.

# The Commodore

I have a model of it here, like the one I gave to the City of New York. Tell me, can you read the inscription on the monument?"

"My eyes aren't so keen any more, Uriah," John Coulter confessed. "You must read it to me."

Uriah read:

> *"Here lies President Thomas Jefferson, Author of the Declaration of American Independence, of the Statute of Virginia for Religious Liberty, and Father of Virginia University."*

"He wrote it himself. Notice, Mr. Coulter, that among all his great achievements, Jefferson chose the Statute for Religious Liberty. If I loved him for nothing else, I would love him for that."

"And what would you choose for your monument, Uriah," asked John Coulter, playfully?

Uriah said, "I hope what will be written on my tomb will be,

> *"He abolished flogging in the United States Navy."*

I should be content with that."

"I have heard of your crusade on the subject, Uriah. Is it wise? Did it not lead to your court-martial?"

"No good officer in the Navy but has his court-martials," replied Uriah, laughing. "Just because I stuck a few feathers on a boy instead of giving him twelve stripes. I have been writing articles on the subject, and if the Lord lets me live to do it, I will yet accomplish my aim."

# The Commodore

"I have read one of your articles," said Coulter. "It was quite convincing—but some of the old Navy men don't admire you for it."

"No matter," replied Uriah. "Come up to the house now, and I'll show you the prettiest ship model you ever saw—a model of *Vandalia,* my command, and the first ship in the Navy in which there was no flogging."

The two men strolled back to the house. On the way, John Coulter admired the fine groves of trees, planted by Jefferson, and the beautiful hedges, well-clipped and tended.

"I do much of the work myself," Uriah explained. "Sometimes when I am out gardening, in my farm clothes, visitors come to Monticello. If I don't like their looks, I pretend to be the gardener. 'Sorry, Captain Levy is in New York,' I tell them, 'but I am sure that he wouldn't mind if you looked around.' Some of them try to tip me, or ask me to sell them slips from Jefferson's trees or other souvenirs. Then I say, 'Thank you very much, but Captain Levy pays me well enough.' I venture to think they go home thinking simple Virginian gardeners are very honest!"

"You always enjoyed a joke," John Coulter commented.

"I enjoy making fun of pretentious people," Uriah admitted. "The other day there was a parcel of females here, very hoity-toity people from the North, told me, as gardener, it seemed a shame that such a fine old place had fallen into the hands of a Jew. I took them all through the place. You'll notice I have my family portraits on the walls—that picture of my Aunt, Madame Noel (her

husband was slain by the guillotine in the French Revolution)—is by Sir Joshua Reynolds, and some of the
others are equally fine. Well, sir, when those females
asked me whom the portraits represented, I told them
they were all members of the Jefferson family and they
took it all for truth—pointed out resemblances to Jefferson in the pictures, and so on."

"It served the good ladies right," exclaimed Coulter,
laughing.

He admired the *Vandalia* model and asked Uriah
whether he would not rather command such a vessel than
be a farmer here at Monticello.

"Aye, that I would. But if the Navy doesn't see it
my way, what can I do? I am not disposed to sulk. I shall
yet have another command."

"And what is to become of Monticello if you go to
sea again?"

"Never fear, it will be well taken care of. And as I
have said, by my will, I intend to leave the place to the
nation—if Congress turns it down, then to the State of
Virginia. If Virginia is ungrateful enough to the memory of her great son—then to the Shearith Israel in New
York and the Mikveh Israel in Philadelphia, my two
Hebrew Congregations."

"Do you mean it to be a sort of Mt. Vernon?"

"No, it is too remote for that. I am going to put in
my will that I wish it used for a school for the sons of
petty officers in the Navy whose fathers are dead, and
I am going to leave all my estate in trust to support the
school. I have it all in mind, Mr. Coulter. The children

are to be twelve to sixteen years old and are to be taught the elements of farming."

"What a wonderful thing to do, Uriah."

"It is only just. No one is dependent on me. But I am going to make a further stipulation in my will—I mean to especially require that no professors be employed in the school. My intention, you see, is charity and usefulness and not for the purposes of pomp."

"Suppose there are not enough sons of petty officers who desire to enroll?"

"I have thought of that, too. Then the next place shall go to the sons of seamen in the Navy. There will surely be enough then. In any case, both Hebrews and Christians are to have equal right of entrance."

"You are a remarkable man, Uriah," said John.

"I am American, a sailor, and a Jew," replied Uriah. "Also, a farmer of sorts. At all events, I don't intend to die for a long time to come, and meanwhile, I intend to enjoy Monticello—at least until the blasted Navy sees fit to give me another command."

$\star$

$\star$ $\star$

$\star$ ## 23 $\star$

$\star$ $\star$

$\star$

SO THE years passed, pleasantly enough for Uriah, with winters in New York—summers at Monticello, and occasional trips to London and Paris to renew old friendships. Uriah prospered, and he got much satisfaction when an Act of Congress finally prohibited flogging in the Navy. Whatever happened, he felt that that was an accomplishment worthy of a man.

His bachelor's life was rather lonely. Since his early love for the French noblewoman, he had often fancied himself in love with one or another of the beautiful and accomplished ladies he had met, but had never seriously contemplated marriage.

Then one day the middle-aged Captain met and discovered Miss Virginia Lopez, a young lady who happened to be the vivacious and amusing daughter of one of his own sisters who had married the scion of a noted Jamaica Jewish family. Virginia Lopez had been sent by her father to a seminary for young ladies in England, and while she was there, having suffered financial misfortunes in the West Indies, Lopez decided to leave Jamaica and come to the United States.

He settled in New York, and when his daughter, Virginia, came home from school, it was to New York, rather than to her native island.

When she met Uriah, he found himself irresistibly attracted to her, and she was flattered and pleased by the interest of the famous Captain Levy. It wasn't long until, to the astonishment of Uriah's friends, the Captain proposed marriage to Virginia and was accepted.

Again to the surprise of Uriah's friends, who predicted that the marriage would be a failure because of the great difference in the ages of the parties, the marriage was a great success.

Soon after the marriage, Virginia's father died, and Uriah took his bride to Monticello. Virginia's poise and natural grace stood her in great stead as mistress of the Jefferson mansion. If Uriah's friends had enjoyed visiting him there before, they were now enchanted. The great and the famous came to Monticello, and Uriah found happiness in entertaining his guests. Virginia also had a manner which was a complement to Uriah's natural abruptness. She was diplomatic and clever, and very devoted, not only to her husband, but to his career. The exploits of his youth had made him famous, and his crusade against the lash had made him popular, and had it not been for a catastrophic event which occurred in 1855, Uriah would probably have lived out the rest of his life quietly—always hopeful of new commands, but content, while waiting, to live the kind of pleasant life he was living.

But in 1855, Congress, in a periodic fit of economy, decreed that officers in the Navy, no matter how long they might have served, might be dropped from the rolls. Uriah paid little heed to the passage of the Act, but soon after its passage, he wrote to the Secretary of the Navy one of his periodic and routine requests for active service. He was shocked—almost annihilated in spirit—when he received a brusque note stating that he had been dropped from the rolls, and addressing him as Uriah P. Levy, *formerly* Captain, U. S. Navy.

Nothing so devastating had happened to him since the day so many years before, when he had stood on the shore on the Isle of May and watched his mate piratically run away with his ship.

How could the Navy behave with such gross injustice? Was it because he was a Jew? Two hundred non-Jews had also been dropped at the same time, and there were other Jewish officers of lower rank than Uriah, who had not been dropped.

"It is the same old martinets," he told Virginia. "They hate me because they can no longer flog; they have always hated me for being human, as well as Jewish, and having come up from the ranks. Well, I'll show them! I do not know what the other two hundred have done, but I propose to fight."

"Of course, you will fight," exclaimed Virginia. "And you will win this battle as you have won so many others."

Now all was activity for Uriah. He demanded a review

of his dismissal before a court of inquiry, and when he received such a review, set about preparing his case with ferocious energy.

He and Virginia went to Washington, Philadelphia and New York, gathering affidavits regarding every phase of his naval career.

It was November 1857 when the court of inquiry finally convened in Washington. For a whole year and a half, Uriah had driven himself on the quest for evidence, obsessed with the necessity to obtain restoration to his Naval Captain's status.

The court was formal, dignified, and interested. The cabal of officers who had brought Uriah low had spared no effort to prepare the case against him. Statements from his naval officer enemies were spread at length on the record. One said, under oath, "His temper and disposition were not such as to promote good order in the service. His general reputation is not good."

Others said he wasn't fit for command. This, of the man who had taken the *Vandalia* into hostile waters of the Gulf of Mexico, and returned with his mission accomplished!

The full reports of all six of Uriah's court-martials were read into the record.

"It's ridiculous," Uriah stormed. "Where I was found not guilty, how can the fact that I was charged have anything to do with my worthiness?"

Uriah wrung from reluctant enemy witnesses grudging admissions that his seamanship was not open to question. But was he fit to be an officer and a gentleman? His enemies insisted he was not.

# The Commodore

Over and over the same objections, the same charges were made—vague accusations, but as Uriah told Virginia, it was the unspoken charges which were really before the court: his leniency to the common sailor, his religion, his failure to follow the traditional course.

"If I could call them out to a duel," Uriah told Virginia, "we should soon see. Better yet—give me command of a ship, give them one, and send us out against each other, and see who strikes his colors. Those fellows are parade ground officers; they believe the Navy is a sort of society or club, and they don't want a Uriah Levy for a member. But we'll spike their guns yet. This battle is not only for me, but for those who come after."

At length, it was Uriah's turn. Now he unloosed a broadside of affidavits and testimony. He traced his entire career, produced his orders and showed how he had carried them out. Early in his defense, his opponent, the Judge-Advocate, was forced to admit that Uriah's seamanship was not in question; it became almost entirely a question of his personality. All the ghosts of the past were called up; he proved his valor and his integrity. His witnesses were such men as Commodore Stewart, his old commander when Uriah was a young sailing master on the *Franklin;* Commodore Mayo; Commodore Voorhees, and other high ranking officers who were not members of the hostile cabal. Officers who had served with him when he was a lieutenant, and officers who had served under him when he was in command, all came forward and added their voices.

Then came his civilian witnesses; former governors, an Assistant Secretary of the Treasury, physicians, bank-

ers, men prominent in every phase of American life, testified to Uriah's character and worthiness to serve the country he loved. Altogether, fifty-three witnesses were produced on Uriah's behalf, and more than two hundred documents exhibited to the court.

Finally, Uriah himself made an impassioned speech in his own behalf. He referred to his service, his hopes and ambitions, and his fitness. When he came to speak of his religion, he was carried away by his feelings and exclaimed,

"For with those who would now deny to me, because of my religious faith, the restoration to which, by half-a-century of witnesses, I have proved myself entitled, what is it but to place those who profess my faith under the ban of incapacity?

"Mine is the case of every Israelite in the Union. I need not speak to you of their number. They are unsurpassed by any portion of our people in loyalty to the Constitution and to the Union; in their quiet obedience to the laws; and in the cheerfulness with which they contribute to the public burdens. Many of them have been distinguished by their liberal donations to the general interests of education and of charity; in some cases, too, of which the name of Judah Touro will remind you—to charities controlled by Christians. And all my brethren in this land—as well those of foreign birth as of American descent—how rarely does any one of them become a charge on your State or Municipal treasuries! How largely do they all contribute to the activities of trade; to the interests of commerce; to the stock of public wealth! Are all these to be proscribed? And is this to be done while we retain the noble language of our Constitution? Is this language to be spoken to the ear, but broken to the hope, of my race? Are the thousands of Judah and the ten thousands of Israel, in their dispersions throughout the earth, who look to America as a land bright with promise—are they now to learn to their sorrow and dismay that we, too, have sunk into the mire of religious intolerance and bigotry? And are American Christians now to begin the persecution of the Jews? Of the Jews, who stand among them the representatives of the patriarchs and prophets; the Jews, to whom were committed the Oracles of God; the Jews, from whom these Oracles have been received, and who are the living witnesses of their truth; the Jews, from whom came the founder of Christianity; the Jews, to whom as Christians themselves believe, have been made promises of greatness and glory, in whose fulfilment are bound up the hopes, not only of the remnant of Israel, but of all the races of men?

"And think not, if you once enter this career, that it can be limited to the Jew. What is my case today, if you yield to this injustice, may tomorrow be that of the Roman Catholic or the Unitarian, the Episcopalian or the Methodist, the Presbyterian or the Baptist. There is but one safeguard; and this is to be found in an honest, whole-hearted, inflexible support of the wise, the just, the impartial guarantee of the Constitution. I have the fullest confidence that you will faithfully adhere to this guarantee; and, therefore, with like confidence, I leave my destiny in your hands."

Uriah had finished.

# The Commodore

There was only one answer an American court could give.

Captain Uriah Phillips Levy was restored to the rank of captain in the United States Navy, with seniority, as though he had never been dropped.

Shortly after, with a characteristic lack of resentment over his victory, the Navy ordered him to active service—and gave him one of the highest posts in the service. He was ordered to command the *S. S. Macedonian,* finest ship in the Mediterranean Squadron—and told that in a few months Commodore LaVallette, the present commodore, was due to be relieved, and that he, Uriah, might expect to become commodore and command the squadron!

★
★　　　★

★ **24** ★

★　　　★
★

THAT spring of 1858 the nation was veering on the course which was to end with the great clash of arms which became the Civil War. Even though the Presidential election to select President Buchanan's successor was a year and a half off, the issues were being hotly debated. This was the year of the Lincoln-Douglas debate, the year when men were beginning to say fearfully that there seemed no way out by which the questions might be solved. But for Uriah, it was a year of triumph. Restored to his rank in the Navy, master of Monticello, married to the charming and vivacious Virginia, and given the command he had so long desired, Uriah was happier than he had ever been in his life. When he arrived in Boston to oversee the refitting of the *Macedonian* before taking the vessel to the Mediterranean, he found himself a celebrity. He had become a symbol of the triumph of Jeffersonian democracy. His fight with the small minority of navy officers who had wished him harm for daring to be a Jew, as well as an officer, and with the larger minority who hated him because he had never gone through the regular officer training of a midshipman, had been a dramatic proof to many that the Republic meant what they had hoped—a nation in which anyone of ability, whatever his religion, whatever his school or background, could have any rank in public service for which he was fitted.

Many young naval officers looked up to Uriah now, as one who had defied the old martinets and survived. Poets and sages looked up to him as a valiant and untiring fighter, not only for his own rights, but for the rights of all who suffered from injustice; and also as one who believed in merciful punishment, when punishment was needed, and did not need to rely for his strength on flogging his unwilling inferiors.

Uriah had his share of vanity and he was well aware of his position and enjoyed it.

"If I behave myself, the Navy will treat me well," he told Virginia. "Even the old fools who fought me have an American tradition of sportsmanship. Now that they have lost, they will treat me as a winner, never fear."

"But now that you have a command, think how lonely your Virginia will be, while her hero is sailing away," she teased.

He smiled, "Haven't I promised you, you are to meet me abroad."

"Yes, but that will mean sailing on a passenger ship all alone and waiting for you in a foreign country."

"I think not. I think not. Virginia, prepare for a

# The Commodore

surprise. I have asked to take you along with me, on the *Macedonian!*"

"Uriah! I never heard of such a thing," Virginia was wide-eyed with delight.

"For a very good reason," Uriah replied. "I don't think it has ever occurred before in modern times. But why not? I shall ask the Navy, and in the Department's present mood, I doubt they will cross me in anything so reasonable. Anyone with half a mind can see that a young orphan bride should not be denied her husband's protection just because he happens to be a captain in the Navy. Especially this captain!"

Then Uriah read her the request he was making to take his wife along on his cruise to the Mediterranean.

Uriah was not surprised when he received his answer, though everyone else was. It wasn't customary, said the kind, old Navy Department—but after all, since she was an orphan—he could take her alone as far as the first European port!

So, on an unbelievable day that spring, Uriah took his Virginia with him, hoisted sail on the *Macedonian,* and sailed out of Boston for Leghorn, Italy. Henry Wadsworth Longfellow, an admirer of Uriah's, came to the ship to wish the couple well. "It is incredible," he exclaimed, "a veritable second honeymoon, and on a war vessel," and he presented Virginia with a copy of his *Psalm of Life,* suitably inscribed.

Arrived in Europe, there was a constant round of parties for Virginia, and the pleasant duties of a peacetime naval command for Uriah. Because of his fame, all doors were open to him. A British admiral gave a dance in his honor. "What a pleasure," exclaimed Uriah. "Once I was impressed into your Navy, once I was your prisoner of war; now I am your guest."

In Naples he and Virginia were invited to spend Yom Kippur with the Rothschilds of banking house fame. They maintained a private synagogue in their residence, and Uriah and his wife spent the day in prayer with their hosts and other guests.

Baron Karl Rothschild was most interested in Uriah's descriptions of America.

"I have heard your story," said Rothschild. "Does it not discourage you? Surely in a nation founded upon religious liberty you ought not to have been subject to attack in your public life because you are a Jew."

"Baron Rothschild," Uriah replied, "I quote from Thomas Jefferson, one of the greatest of Americans, whose home, incidentally, is now my home—said Jefferson—'I steer my bark with Hope in the head, leaving Fear astern'—and he pointed out that when he drew the bill for establishing religious freedom in the United States, it met with opposition. There was a proposal made that the words 'Jesus Christ' should be inserted in the preamble, and the proposal was voted down by a great majority, in proof that they meant to comprehend, within the mantle of the protection of that bill, the Jew and the Gentile, the Christian, and the Mohammedan, the Hindu and infidel of every denomination. That, sir, is still true, and I know will always be true in the United States. Do not forget, sir, that the Jew is not alien to the United States. He has been there, a part of

# The Commodore

the United States, since there has been a United States. The glory of the creation of our Republic belongs no less—and no more—to him than to every other element of our population. He is not in the United States on the sufferance of some ruler, or of an indigenous people; he is there as he *has* been there, an integral part."

"Then is he less a Jew?" asked Baron Rothschild.

"No, he is more," responded Uriah. "For he is a Jew by his own choice, as I am. He cringes to none, he demands and expects equality, and by the very nature of our Republic, he cannot fail to receive it."

"And your own troubles—?" asked the Baron.

"Were only sufficient to put me upon my mettle, to resolve to be better than all others in my profession, to serve as an example for all Jewish officers to come."

"In that, I am sure you have succeeded," the Baron exclaimed in a flattering tone.

So time passed, and the pleasant round of duties took Uriah—and Virginia—further on their Mediterranean round. In the Holy Land, Uriah had a ton of soil put on board, to be conveyed back to the Shearith Israel in New York as a gift from him, for use at funerals, where a handful of earth from the Holy Land was traditionally thrown upon the coffin of the deceased.

Then there was Egypt, with Virginia gaining entrance into a Pasha's Harem, and reporting wide-eyed the luxuries enjoyed by the stout Oriental ladies she found there.

At last came the greatest day of all—October 20, 1859, when Commodore LaValette having been relieved, Uriah

# The Commodore

Phillips Levy succeeded him and raised the wide banner of Commodore of the Mediterranean Squadron upon his ship.

Commodore Levy! He had come to the end of the voyage of his ambition. Alone and valiant, he had fought his way from cabin boy to the top command in the service of the country he loved. Without compromising his religious faith, his honor, or his principles, he had proven that his faith in the great Republic had been justified—that faith which told him that as long as that Republic stood, men would be free to be whatever their abilities allowed them to be—if they were valiant enough and strong enough, and valued the freedom they had won above all price.

He watched the bright pennant blowing in the Mediterranean breeze and exclaimed, "I salute the emblem of the victory I have won—a victory not mine alone, but one in which all who come after, along the course I have set, may share!"

ND NOW it was the spring of 1861, and there
was the tall, swaggering old commodore, waiting in the White House, talking to Tad and
Willie Lincoln, talking to young John Hay, the President's secretary, waiting to be received by Abraham
Lincoln; dreaming back, while he waited, over the long,
long years—years of the glory of the young Republic,
years in which he himself had risen so high.

When Uriah had hauled down his commodore's pennant on July 14, 1860, at the conclusion of his tour of
duty, he had done so with satisfaction. His career at
sea ended, he had no further ambition for command.
Still an officer in the Navy, he was now the ranking
senior captain; but in the ordinary course, he could look
forward to a pleasant retirement to his beloved Monticello, where he could live the life of a gentleman
farmer, so often desired by the old seafaring man; revise
the book he had written on naval procedures, play host

to the great and the amusing, and enjoy himself in well-earned leisure.

But he had not reckoned on the tremendous and earth-shaking events of the year 1860. Suddenly (though now everyone realized it had been a long time brewing), the great storm swept down upon the nation and threatened to tear it to pieces. The Presidential Conventions, held in an atmosphere of turbulence, led into an election campaign of unprecedented passion. The election of Abraham Lincoln had stirred Uriah. Here was a man who had never been what corresponded to a midshipman in civil life; a man truly and democratically sprung from the people, come to power. Uriah prayed earnestly that the new President might avert the catastrophe of civil war and the break-up of the Union.

Like many another patriot, he became more and more alarmed as event followed event, and when Sumter was fired upon, he told Virginia he could wait no longer, he must return to active service and a chance to serve the Union.

Up from Monticello they came to New York, and as it became evident that secession was inevitable, and that secession meant war, Uriah would hear of nothing but that he must go to see the President.

"It is too dangerous. Washington may be taken any day," Virginia pleaded. "Write or telegraph the President, but do not go."

"I will neither write nor telegraph," he exclaimed. "Don't you recall that I wrote for service in the Mexican War and did not get it. This war, if it comes, will be

# The Commodore

fought on the sea, as well as the land. The southern ports must be blockaded. Steam vessels, as well as sail, will be engaged. It may be the most stupendous naval war in history."

Virginia was not cruel. She did not say—"but it will be a war of youth, Uriah, and you are sixty-nine."

Instead, she gave in, as gracefully as possible, and exclaimed, "I was not with you when you sailed into strange and hostile harbors. I suppose my commodore can take care of himself along the Potomac."

So he had come, and here he was, explaining to young Lincoln that he couldn't say the Lord's Prayer backward. Had I had it in my heart to say the Lord's Prayer at any time, life might have been a little easier, he thought. But I chose the prayers of my fathers, and I am glad. Whatever I have been, I have always been myself, and never did anything merely to curry favor with another.

"So you want to go to sea, and you are nearly eleven," said Uriah to Willie Lincoln.

"Yes, sir, but I would rather be a Zouave than anything."

Suddenly, the door to the inner room opened and a group of men came through it and into the chamber where Uriah was sitting. It was the Cabinet members, breaking away after the session. There they all were, looking like the cartoons in *Vanity Fair,* Seward and Stanton and Chase and the rest, talking gravely and earnestly to each other.

The departing Cabinet members paid no attention

to Uriah. One or two stopped for a hello to the boys, and all waved in greeting to John Hay, who rose and went into the inside room.

In a moment he returned.

"Boys, your pa is busy now, but he'll see you upstairs in half an hour. He says to be good and not to make any noise."

The two boys let out whoops like Indians and rushed out of the room.

John Hay smiled. "Mr. Lincoln is the only one who never hears them," he said, laughing. "The President will see you now, Commodore."

★

★　　　★

★ **26** ★

★　　　★

★

MR. LINCOLN was just as homely as Uriah
had pictured him, and just as human. The
President was sitting back in his chair, slumped
down on the small of his back and with his big feet rest-
ing on the Cabinet table.

"Come in, come in, Commodore," he exclaimed in
his rather high-pitched drawl. "Excuse me if I don't
rise to shake your hand. One of the few privileges the
President has these days is to put his feet on the table if
he has a mind to. At least until the Rebs come to steal
the table right out from under them. Come right on over
here and sit you down in the Secretary of State's chair,
Commodore."

Uriah sat down and the President grasped his hand in
friendly greeting.

"Don't mind me," the President went on. "I wouldn't
talk like this to a stranger. But you're no stranger to

me by reputation, Commodore. You and I have a lot in common."

"Thank you, Mr. President. One thing I know we have in common is we both know the Union must and will be saved."

"Yes, we will save it, never fear. I hear the Rebs have overrun Monticello. I suppose that's why you've come to see me; that's why so many come. 'Save my property, Mr. President.' "

"You may be sure I would not come on so unworthy a project. Monticello will be saved when the nation is saved. I am giving it to the nation by my will."

"If it hasn't been captured by our side when that will is probated, it may prove a powerful incentive to our boys," the President teased. "Join the army and save Monticello. We ought to tell them to try that slogan over at the War Department."

Uriah laughed. Wasn't it wonderful how this man, with the terrible weight of the war on his shoulders, could pause to josh him. He was like a great sea captain sailing into the enemy, pausing to tease a cabin boy.

"Mr. President," Uriah continued, "I haven't come to save Monticello, nor to bring you a plan to save the Union. I have come as a matter of simple duty. I have little to offer my country for all it has given to me and mine, but what little I have, I must offer. First, my sword. I pray you, sir, to allow me to draw it once more for the Union before I die. Send me anywhere—I will serve in the most humble capacity, but do me the honor to use me in the naval service. This is my first request."

"I'm mighty pleased to hear it, Commodore. Let's

see now, you're a mite up in years, if I recall—not that you look it."

"I am, and therefore, I do not ask for the command which would be due my rank. I will take anything at all, if only I can be useful."

"Well, now, that's right good of you. Wish some of my generals would talk that way. Mostly, with them, it's rank or ruin. I'll have to talk to the Secretary of the Navy about that. Hay, Hay," he called. Abraham Lincoln took his feet off the table and turned to look at John Hay as he entered in response to the summons.

"Hay, we'll have to find the Commodore here something in his line. Let me see, don't I seem to remember that you went through—and survived—quite a few court-martials in your navy life?"

"Six court-martials and a court of inquiry," Uriah admitted.

"Yes, you would have made a good lawyer. On the right side, too. Didn't believe in flogging, I remember. Commodore, I doubt we can send you to sea—but all that court-martial experience ought not to go to waste. Hay, tell the Navy Secretary I want Commodore Levy assigned to court-martial duty here in Washington. Turn about is fair play. We'll let the Commodore do the court-martialling. He won't be so likely to let the old Navy men get around him as some others I can think of. Tell me, Commodore, will you serve?"

"I'll serve in any capacity, sir."

"Good. It will be done. What was your second purpose. I own I'm curious about what else you wish to do."

"I wish to give all I own to the cause," said Uriah.

# The Commodore

"All you own? You don't mean Monticello. That would be hard to lay our hands on at the moment."

"I mean all I possess, except for my house in New York, where my wife and I live. I am not a millionaire, Mr. President, but I have managed to accumulate a sufficiency. I would like to give it to the government to help pay the expense of putting down the rebellion."

Abraham Lincoln looked up with real curiosity. "That's a fine offer, Commodore. If there were more like you—but we couldn't ask you to do a thing like that."

"It would only be a payment a little in advance," explained Uriah. "Under the terms of my will (my wife being already provided for), the residue of my estate is to be left to the United States to endow Monticello as a school for certain poor boys, sons of warrant officers in the Navy. Instead of that, I'm willing to give it all now for the defense of the Union."

"Well now, Commodore, I don't think that's necessary, and we aren't going to take your offer. I thank you for it. I do, indeed. If every man gave all he possessed to the United States at this moment, we wouldn't have to levy the kind of taxes the Secretary of the Treasury says we'll need. But we'll not need all your money, Commodore. We're going to whip the rebels and we must try to do it so that we have something to start over with, after we've done it. We don't want to destroy the structure of the country; we want to be ready for peace, as well as war. I'll be obliged to you if you'll buy government bonds with your money when we need to issue them, but buy them as an investment, not as a gift, the

# The Commodore

way I intend to do. Your kind and my kind have a big stake in this country, Commodore. We all started poor, and the country's rich even though some of us may not be. Now, Commodore, you run along back to New York and wait orders. We're going to use you right enough, in this court-martial duty, and maybe more active duty than that, before we're through. We'll tax away some of your money, too, along with that of everyone else."

Commodore Levy arose.

John Hay, standing in the doorway, having overheard the latter part of the conversation, said, "And don't forget to learn the Lord's Prayer backward, Commodore, so that you can help out another member of the Lincoln family when you next visit us."

"Have those boys been at the Commodore?" asked Abraham Lincoln. "I'd better go up to them now and keep them out of mischief."

He turned to Uriah, his dark eyes full of animation. "Fellows like you and me have got to stand together, Commodore," he exclaimed. "That's what the Union means. We'll see to it that a man can say any prayer he pleases, and refuse to say any he doesn't please. We won't flog our boys if they act up; we won't submit to threats or force of arms; and we won't quit making this the kind of country it was meant to be."

The two men smiled at each other as Uriah stepped aside to allow Abraham Lincoln to go first through the open door.